500 FAMILY CAMPSITES

Assessments of the campsites are based on the experience of the AA Caravan & Camping Inspectors on the occasion of their visit(s) and therefore descriptions given in this guide necessarily contain an element of subjective opinion which may not reflect or dictate a reader's own opinion on another occasion. AA Media Limited strives to ensure accuracy in this guide at the time of printing. Due to the constantly evolving nature of the information this may be subject to change. AA Media Limited will gratefully receive any advice from our readers of any necessary updated information.

Website addresses are included where they have been supplied and specified by the respective establishments. Such websites are not under the control of AA Media Limited and as such the AA has no control over them and will not accept any liability in respect of any and all matters whatsoever relating to such websites including access, content, material and functionality. By including the addresses of third party websites the AA does not intend to solicit business or offer any security to any person in any country, directly or indirectly.

Co-ordinator, AA Caravan & Camping Scheme – David Hancock

Front cover: (top) Tummel Valley Holiday Park, Tummel Bridge, Perth & Kinross; (middle) Park Cliffe Camping & Caravan Estate, Windermere, Cumbria; (bottom) Ranch Caravan Park, Honeybourne, Worcestershire

All other photographs: 1 AA/Peter Wilson

Printed in China by Leo Paper Products

Directory compiled by AA Lifestyle Guides Department and managed in the Librios Information Management System and generated from the AA establishment database system.

Published by AA Publishing, a trading name of AA Media Limited, whose registered office is Fanum House, Basing View, Basingstoke, Hampshire, RG21 4EA.

Registered number 06112600

A CIP catalogue record for this book is available from the British Library

ISBN: 978-0-7495-6463-6
A04301

Welcome to the Guide

This mini guide is aimed at families with children looking for the right caravan or camping park for their holiday. Within its pages you'll find parks of all kinds, from busy, action-packed holiday centres to small sites handily located near beaches or other attractions. All of the sites are child friendly, the great majority offering a play area at least, and many also offering swimming pools, tennis and other facilities. Do check with the park when you book that all your requirements will be met. To find out more about the inspection process and the other sites in the scheme visit theAA.com

The AA Campsite Classification Scheme

AA parks are classified on a 5-point scale according to their style and range of facilities they offer. As the number of pennants increases, so the quality and variety of facilities is generally greater.

► One Pennant Parks offer a drinking water supply, chemical disposal point, and refuse collection. They may or may not have toilets and washing facilities.

►► Two Pennant Parks additionally offer seperate washrooms including at least 2 toilets and 2 wash basins per 30 pitches per sex, hot and cold water directly to each basin, and dishwashing facilities.

►►► Three Pennant Parks offer modern or modernised toilets with, additionally, at least one private shower cubicle per 35 pitches per sex, electric hook-ups, automatic laundry and children's playground.

►►►► Four Pennant Parks are of a very high quality, especially in the toilets which offer vanitory-style wash basins including some in lockable cubicles, or en suite shower/washing/toilet cubicles.

►►►►► Five Pennant Parks are some of an outstanding quality, and offer some fully-serviced pitches, along with first class toilet facilities including en suite cubicles.

A seperate HOLIDAY CENTRE category indicates that full day and night holiday entertainment is offered, including sports, leisure and recreational facilities, and a choice of eating outlets.

The quality percentage score shows a comparison between sites within the same pennant rating. The score runs between 50% and 80%.

A new category for parks catering only for recreational vehicles (RV) has been created, (no toilet facilities are provided at these sites).

Sample Entry

1 **EDGCUMBE**

2 ►►► 77% **Retanna Holiday Park**

TR13 0EJ

3 ☎ 01326 340643 01326 340643

e-mail: retannaholpark@btconnect.com

web: www.retanna.co.uk

4 **dir:** *100mtrs off A394, signed*

5 * £15-£19 £15-£19

6 Open Apr-Oct Last arrival 21.00hrs Last departure noon

7 A small family-owned and run park in a rural location midway between Falmouth and Helston. Its well-sheltered grassy pitches make this an ideal location for visiting the lovely beaches and towns nearby. An 8 acre site with 24 touring pitches and 23 statics.

8 **Leisure:**
Facilities:
Services:
Within 3 miles:

9 **Notes:** No pets, no disposable BBQs, no open fires. Free use of fridge/freezer in laundry room

1 **Location** Place names are listed alphabetically within each county.

2 **Site Name & Rating**

3 **Contact details**

4 **Directions** Brief directions from a recognisable point, such as a main road, are included in each entry.

5 **Charges** Rates given after each appropriate symbol (Caravan, Campervan, Tent) are overnight costs for one caravan or tent, one car and two adults, or one motorhome and two adults. The prices vary according to the number of people in the party, but some parks have a fixed fee per pitch regardless of the number of people. Please note that some sites charge separately for certain facilities, including showers; and some sites charge a different rate for pitches with or without electricity. Prices are subject to change during the currency of this publication. * If this symbol appears before the prices, it indicates that the site has not advised us of the prices for 2010; they relate to 2009.

6 **Opening, Arrival & Departure Times** Parks are not necessarily open all year and while most sites permit arrivals at any time, checking beforehand is advised.

7 **Description** This is based on information supplied by the AA inspector at the time of the last visit. The brief description of the site includes the number of touring pitches and hardstandings. We include the number of static caravan pitches in order to give an indication of the nature and size of the site. Please note: The AA pennant classification is based on the touring pitches and the facilities only. AA inspectors do not visit or report on caravans or chalets for hire. The AA takes no responsibility for the condition of rented accommodation and can take no action in the event of complaints relating to them.

8 **Symbols & Abbreviations** These are divided into Leisure, Facilities, Services and Within 3 miles sections. Explanations can be found on page 6.

9 **Notes** This includes information about any restrictions the site would like their visitors to be aware of and any additional facilities.

As most sites now accept credit and debit cards, we have only indicated those that don't accept cards.

Facilities for disabled visitors The final stage (Part III) of the Disability Discrimination Act came into force in 2004. This means that service providers may be required to make permanent physical adjustments and adaptations to their premises; for example, the installation of ramps, hand rails and toilet and shower facilities suitable for use by visitors with restricted mobility.

♿ If a site has told us that they provide facilities for disabled visitors their entry in the guide will include this symbol. The sites in this guide should be aware of their responsibilities under the Act. However, we recommend that you always telephone in advance to ensure the site you have chosen has facilities to suit your needs. For further information see the government website www.disability.gov.uk

Useful information It is advisable to book in advance. Check if a reservation entitles you to a particular pitch. Most sites, except those catering for tents only, will have a chemical disposal point. Most also have electric hook-ups, for which you can ususally hire cables if necessary. If disposal point of hook up is important to you, please check when booking. Most sites accept dogs, although some will refuse certain breeds, so again, it is best to check when booking.

Symbols & Abbreviations

	Bath
	Shower
	Electric Shaver
	Hairdryer
	Ice Pack Facility
	Disabled Facilities
	Public Telephone
	Shop on Site or within 200yds
	Mobile Shop (calling at least 5 days per week)
	BBQ Area
	Picnic Area
	Dog Exercise Area
	Indoor Swimming Pool
	Outdoor Swimming Pool
	Tennis Court
	Games Room
	Children's Playground
	Stables & Horse Riding
	9/18 hole Golf Course
	Boats for Hire
	Cinema
	Fishing
	Mini Golf
	Watersports
	Separate TV room
T	Toilet Fluid
	Café or Restaurant
	Fast Food/Takeaway
	Baby Care
	Electric Hook Up
	Motorvan Service Point
	Launderette
	Licensed Bar
	Calor Gas
	Camping Gaz
	Battery Charging
BH	Bank holiday/s
Etr	Easter
Whit	Whitsun
dep	departure
fr	from
hrs	hours
m	mile
mdnt	midnight
rdbt	roundabout
rs	restricted service
RV	Recreational Vehicles
U	rating not confirmed
wk	week
wknd	weekend
	no dogs
	no credit or debit cards

RISELEY

►►► 77% Wellington Country Park

Odiham Rd RG7 1SP

☎ 0118 932 6444 0118 932 6445

e-mail: info@wellington-country-park.co.uk

web: www.wellington-country-park.co.uk

dir: *M4 junct 11, A33 south towards Basingstoke. M3 junct 5, B3349 north towards Reading*

Open Mar-Nov Last arrival 17.30hrs Last departure 13.00hrs

A peaceful woodland site set within an extensive country park, which comes complete with lakes and nature trails. There's also a herd of Red and Fallow deer that roam the meadow area. Ideal for M4 travellers. An 80 acre site with 72 touring pitches, 10 hardstandings.

Leisure:

Facilities:

Services:

Within 3 miles:

Notes: No open fires, pets must be kept on leads. Miniature railway, crazy golf, maze, animal corner

CAMBRIDGE

►►► 72% Cambridge Camping & Caravanning Club Site

19 Cabbage Moor, Great Shelford CB2 5NB

☎ 01223 841185

dir: *M11 junct 11 onto A1309 signed Cambridge. At 1st lights turn right. After 0.5m follow site sign on left*

Open 2 Apr-2 Nov Last arrival 21.00hrs Last departure noon

A popular, open site close to Cambridge and the M11, surrounded by high hedging and trees, with well-maintained toilet facilities. The large rally field is well used. An 11 acre site with 120 touring pitches.

Leisure:

Facilities:

Services:

Within 3 miles:

Notes: Site gates closed 23.00hrs-07.00hrs

HUNTINGDON

►►► 77% The Willows Caravan Park

Bromholme Ln, Brampton PE28 4NE

☎ 01480 437566

e-mail: willows@willows33.freeserve.co.uk

dir: *Exit A14/A1 signed Brampton, follow Huntingdon signs. Site on right close to Brampton Mill pub*

£14-£18 £14-£18 £13-£16

Open Mar-Oct Last arrival 20.00hrs Last departure noon

A small, friendly site in a pleasant setting beside the River Ouse, on the Ouse Valley Walk. Bay areas have been provided for caravans and motorhomes, and planting for screening is gradually maturing. There are launching facilities and free river fishing. A 4 acre site with 50 touring pitches, 10 hardstandings.

Leisure:

Facilities:

Services:

Within 3 miles:

Notes: No cars by tents Dogs must be on leads, ball games on field provided, no generators, no groundsheets, 5mph one-way system. Free book lending/exchange

CODDINGTON

►►►► 82% Manor Wood Country Caravan Park

Manor Wood CH3 9EN

☎ 01829 782990 & 782442

01829 782990

e-mail: info@manorwoodcaravans.co.uk

dir: *From A534 at Barton, turn opposite Cock O'Barton pub signed Coddington. Left in 100yds. Site 0.5m on left*

£12-£21 £12-£21 £12-£21

Open all year (rs Oct-May swimming pool closed) Last arrival 20.30hrs Last departure 11.00hrs

A secluded landscaped park in a tranquil country setting with extensive views towards the Welsh Hills across the Cheshire Plain. This park offers fully-serviced pitches, modern facilities, a heated outdoor pool and tennis courts. Wildlife is encouraged, and lake fishing with country walks and pubs are added attractions. 25 seasonal touring pitches available. An 8 acre site with 45 touring pitches, 38 hardstandings and 12 statics.

Leisure: **Facilities:** **Services:** **Within 3 miles:** **Notes:** No cars by caravans

DELAMERE

►►► Fishpool Farm Caravan Park

Fishpool Rd CW8 2HP

☎ 01606 883970

e-mail: enquiries@fishpoolfarmcaravanpark.co.uk

dir: *From Tarporley take A49 towards Cuddington. Left onto B5152. Continue on B5152 (now Fishpool Rd). Site on right*

£20-£25 £20-£22 £12-£14

Open Mar-Jan Last arrival 19.00hrs Last departure mdnt

This newly developed site on the owner's farm opened in August 2009, replete with shop/reception, a purpose-built toilet block with laundry facilities, a picnic area, and 50 pitches, all with electric hook-up. Plans include a lakeside lodge, coarse fishing, and a nature walk. At the time of going to press the quality % score for this site had not been confirmed. For up-to-date information please see the AA website: theAA.com. A 5.5 acre site with 50 touring pitches.

Leisure: **Facilities:** **Services:** **Within 3 miles:** **Notes:** Dogs must be on leads. Dog walks available

ASHTON

►►► 72% Boscrege Caravan & Camping Park

TR13 9TG

☎ 01736 762231 01736 762152

e-mail: enquiries@caravanparkcornwall.com

dir: *From Helston on A394 turn right in Ashton by Post Office into lane. Site in 1.5m, signed*

Open Mar-Nov Last arrival 22.00hrs Last departure 11.00hrs

A quiet and bright little touring park divided into small paddocks with hedges, and offering plenty of open spaces for children to play in. The family-owned park offers clean, well-painted toilets facilities and neatly trimmed grass. In an Area of Outstanding Natural Beauty at the foot of Tregonning Hill. A 14 acre site with 50 touring pitches and 26 statics.

Leisure:

Facilities:

Services:

Within 3 miles:

Notes: Recreation fields, microwave, nature trail

BLACKWATER

►►► 90% Chiverton Park

East Hill TR4 8HS

☎ 01872 560667 📄 01872 560667

e-mail: chivertonpark@btopenworld.com

dir: *Exit A30 at Chiverton rdbt (Starbucks) onto unclass road signed Blackwater (3rd exit). 1st right, site 300mtrs on right*

* £15-£20 £15-£22 £8-£20

Open 3 Mar-3 Nov (rs Mar-May & mid Sep-Nov limited stock kept in shop) Last arrival 21.00hrs Last departure noon

A small, well-maintained site with some mature hedges dividing pitches, sited midway between Truro and St Agnes. Facilities include a good toilet block and a steam room, sauna and gym. A games room with pool table, and children's outside play equipment prove popular with families. A 4 acre site with 12 touring pitches, 10 hardstandings and 50 statics.

Leisure:

Facilities:

Services:

Within 3 miles:

Notes: No ball games. Drying lines. Wi-fi

BLACKWATER

►►► 81% Trevarth Holiday Park

TR4 8HR

☎ 01872 560266 📄 01872 560379

e-mail: trevarth@lineone.net

web: www.trevarth.co.uk

dir: *Exit A30 at Chiverton rdbt onto B3277 signed St Agnes. At next rdbt take road signed Blackwater. Site on right in 200mtrs*

£11-£16.50 £11-£16.50 £11-£16.50

Open Apr-Oct Last arrival 22.00hrs Last departure 11.30hrs

A neat and compact park with touring pitches laid out on attractive, well-screened high ground adjacent to A30/A39 junction. This pleasant little park is centrally located for touring, and is maintained to a very good standard. A 4 acre site with 30 touring pitches, 10 hardstandings and 21 statics.

Leisure:

Facilities:

Services:

Within 3 miles:

Notes: Recycling facilities

BUDE

89% Sandymouth Holiday Park

Sandymouth Bay EX23 9HW

☎ 01288 352563 01288 354822

e-mail: reception@sandymouthbay.co.uk

web: www.sandymouthbay.co.uk

dir: *Signed off A39 approx 0.5m S of Kilkhampton, 4m N of Bude*

* £18-£28 £18-£28 £12-£22

Open Mar-Oct Last arrival 22.00hrs Last departure 10.00hrs

A bright and friendly holiday park with glorious and extensive sea views from all areas. Now under new ownership, the whole park has undergone a major refurbishment programme. Themed around the eye-catching pirate galleon, this park offers many on-site facilities including an entertainment programme for all age groups. Holiday static caravans are available for hire. A 24 acre site with 100 touring pitches and 132 statics.

Leisure: **Facilities:** **Services:** **Within 3 miles:**

Notes: No pets. Sauna, crazy golf, children's adventure park, arcade, internet access

BUDE

►►►► 82% Budemeadows Touring Park

Widemouth Bay EX23 0NA

☎ 01288 361646 0870 7064825

e-mail: holiday@budemeadows.com

dir: *3m S of Bude on A39. Follow signs after turn to Widemouth Bay. Site accessed via layby*

* £11-£26 £11-£26 £11-£26

Open all year (rs mid Sep-late May shop, bar & pool closed) Last arrival 21.00hrs Last departure 11.00hrs

A very well kept site of distinction, with good quality facilities. Budemeadows is set on a gentle sheltered slope in nine acres of naturally landscaped parkland, surrounded by mature hedges. Just one mile from Widemouth Bay, and three miles from the unspoilt resort of Bude. A 9 acre site with 145 touring pitches, 24 hardstandings.

Leisure:

Facilities:

Services:

Within 3 miles:

Notes: Table tennis, giant chess, baby changing facility. Wi-fi

BUDE

►►►►► 90% Wooda Farm Holiday Park

Poughill EX23 9HJ

☎ 01288 352069 01288 355258

e-mail: enquiries@wooda.co.uk

web: www.wooda.co.uk

dir: *2m E. From A39 at outskirts of Stratton follow unclassified road signed Poughill*

* £12-£28 £12-£28 £12-£28

Open Apr-Oct (rs Apr-May & mid Sep-Oct shop hours limited, bar & takeaway) Last arrival 20.00hrs Last departure noon

Attractive park on raised ground overlooking Bude Bay. Divided into paddocks by hedges and mature trees, with high quality facilities in extensive gardens. Activities provided by large sports hall and hard tennis court, along with children's playground. Holiday statics for hire. A 50 acre site with 200 touring pitches, 72 hardstandings and 55 statics.

Leisure: **Facilities:** **Services:** **Within 3 miles:** **Notes:** Restrictions on certain dog breeds, skateboards, rollerblades & scooters. Coarse fishing, clay pigeon shooting, pets corner, woodland walks. Wi-fi

CAMELFORD

►►►► 85% Juliot's Well Holiday Park

PL32 9RF

☎ 01840 213302 01840 212700

e-mail: juliotswell@breaksincornwall.com

web: www.juliotswell.com

dir: *Through Camelford, A39 at Valley Truckle turn right onto B3266, then 1st left signed Lanteglos, site 300yds on right*

Open all year Last arrival 20.00hrs Last departure 11.00hrs

Set in the wooded grounds of an old manor house, this quiet site enjoys extensive views across the countryside. A rustic inn on site offers occasional entertainment, and there is plenty to do, both on the park and in the vicinity. The superb, fully-serviced toilet facilities are very impressive. There are also self-catering pine lodges, static caravans and five cottages. A 33 acre site with 39 touring pitches and 82 statics.

Leisure:

Facilities:

Services:

Within 3 miles:

Notes: Free cots/high chairs to hire. Wi-fi

CARLYON BAY

►►►► 89% Carlyon Bay Caravan & Camping Park

Bethesda, Cypress Av PL25 3RE

☎ 01726 812735 01726 815496

e-mail: holidays@carlyonbay.net

dir: *Off A390 W of St Blazey, turn left onto A3092 for Par, right in 0.5m. On private road to Carlyon Bay*

Open Etr-3 Oct (rs Etr-mid May & mid Sep-3 Oct swimming pool, take-away & shop closed) Last arrival 21.00hrs Last departure 11.00hrs

An attractive, secluded site set amongst a belt of trees with background woodland. The spacious grassy park offers plenty of on-site attractions, with occasional family entertainment, and it is less than half a mile from a sandy beach. The Eden Project is only two miles away. A 35 acre site with 180 touring pitches, 6 hardstandings.

Leisure:

Facilities:

Services:

Within 3 miles:

Notes: Crazy golf, children's entertainment in Jul & Aug

COVERACK

►►► 77% Little Trevothan Caravan & Camping Park

Trevothan TR12 6SD

☎ 01326 280260

e-mail: sales@littletrevothan.co.uk

web: www.littletrevothan.co.uk

dir: *A3083 onto B3293 signed Coverack, approx 2m after Goonhilly ESS, right at Zoar Garage onto unclass road. Approx 1m, 3rd left. Site 0.5m on left*

* £10-£13 £10-£13 £10-£13

Open Mar-Oct Last arrival 21.00hrs Last departure noon

A secluded site near the unspoilt fishing village of Coverack, with a large recreation area. The nearby sandy beach has lots of rock pools for children to play in, and the many walks both from the park and the village offer stunning scenery. 6 seasonal touring pitches available. A 10.5 acre site with 70 touring pitches, 4 hardstandings and 40 statics.

Leisure:

Facilities:

Services:

Within 3 miles:

Notes: Dogs must be kept on leads

CRACKINGTON HAVEN

►►► 75% Hentervene Holiday Park

EX23 0LF

☎ 01840 230365

e-mail: contact@hentervene.co.uk

dir: *Exit A39 approx 10m SW of Bude (1.5m beyond Wainhouse Corner) onto B3263 signed Boscastle & Crackington Haven. 0.75m to Tresparret Posts junct, right signed Hentervene. Site 0.75m on right*

* £10-£20 £10-£20

Open Mar-Oct Last arrival 21.00hrs Last departure 11.00hrs

This much improved park is set in a rural location a short drive from a golden sandy beach. In an Area of Outstanding Natural Beauty, the pitches are in paddocks bordered by hedges, with a small stream running past. Some pitches are on level terraces, and there are also hardstandings. Static caravans and three pine lodges for self-catering holiday hire. An 11 acre site with 8 touring pitches, 8 hardstandings and 24 statics.

Leisure: **Facilities:** **Services:** **Within 3 miles:** **Notes:** Baby bathroom. Microwave & freezer for campers. Wi-fi

CRANTOCK (NEAR NEWQUAY)

►►►► 85% Trevella Tourist Park

TR8 5EW

☎ 01637 830308 🖷 01637 830155

e-mail: holidays@trevella.co.uk

dir: *Between Crantock & A3075*

Open Etr-Oct

A well established and very well run family site, with outstanding floral displays. Set in a rural area close to Newquay, this attractive park boasts three teeming fishing lakes for the experienced and novice angler, and a superb outdoor swimming pool and paddling area. All areas are neat and clean. A 15 acre site with 313 touring pitches, 53 hardstandings.

Leisure:

Facilities:

Services:

Within 3 miles:

Notes: Crazy golf, badminton

CRANTOCK (NEAR NEWQUAY)

►►► 83% Treago Farm Caravan Site

TR8 5QS

☎ 01637 830277 01637 830277

e-mail: treagofarm@aol.com

dir: *From A3075 (W of Newquay) turn right for Crantock. Site signed beyond village*

Open mid May-mid Sep Last arrival 22.00hrs Last departure 18.00hrs

A grass site in open farmland in a south-facing sheltered valley. This friendly family park has direct access to Crantock and Polly Joke beaches, National Trust land and many natural beauty spots. A 5 acre site with 90 touring pitches and 10 statics.

Leisure:

Facilities:

Services:

Within 3 miles:

CRANTOCK (NEAR NEWQUAY)

►►► 80% Crantock Plains Camping & Caravan Park

TR8 5PH

☎ 01637 830955 & 07967 956897

e-mail: matthew-milburn@btconnect.com

dir: *Exit Newquay on A3075, 2nd right signed to park & Crantock. Site on left in 0.75m on narrow road*

Open Last arrival 22.00hrs Last departure noon

A small rural park with pitches on either side of a narrow lane, surrounded by mature trees for shelter. The family-run park has modern toilet facilities appointed to a good standard. A 6 acre site with 60 touring pitches.

Leisure:

Facilities:

Services:

Within 3 miles:

Notes: No skateboards, dogs on leads at all times

CRANTOCK (NEAR NEWQUAY)

►►► 80% Quarryfield Holiday Park

Quarryfield C&C Park TR8 5RJ

☎ 01637 872792 & 830338
🖷 01637 872792

e-mail: quarryfield@crantockcaravans.orangehome.co.uk

dir: *From A3075 (Newquay-Redruth road) follow Crantock signs. Site signed*

* £12-£18 £12-£18 £12-£18

Open Etr to end Oct (rs May/Sep pool closed) Last arrival 23.00hrs Last departure 10.00hrs

This park has a private path down to the dunes and golden sands of Crantock Beach, about ten minutes away, and it is within easy reach of all that Newquay has to offer, particularly for families. The park has new, very modern facilities, and provides plenty of amenities. A 10 acre site with 145 touring pitches and 43 statics.

Leisure:
Facilities:
Services:
Within 3 miles:
Notes: No campfires, quiet after 22.30hrs

CUBERT

►►► 78% Cottage Farm Touring Park

Treworgans TR8 5HH

☎ 01637 831083

web: www.cottagefarmpark.co.uk

dir: *From A392 towards Newquay, left onto A3075 towards Redruth. In 2m right signed Cubert, right again in 1.5m signed Crantock, left in 0.5m*

* £11-£15 £11-£15 £11-£15

Open Apr-Oct Last arrival 22.30hrs Last departure noon

A small grassy touring park nestling in the tiny hamlet of Treworgans, in sheltered open countryside close to a lovely beach at Holywell Bay. This quiet family-run park boasts very good quality facilities. A 2 acre site with 45 touring pitches, 2 hardstandings and 1 static.

Facilities:
Services:
Within 3 miles:
Notes: Pets allowed from Apr-mid Jul & in Sep

EDGCUMBE

►►► 77% Retanna Holiday Park

TR13 0EJ

☎ 01326 340643 01326 340643

e-mail: retannaholpark@btconnect.com

web: www.retanna.co.uk

dir: *100mtrs off A394, signed*

* £15-£19 £15-£19

Open Apr-Oct Last arrival 21.00hrs Last departure noon

A small family-owned and run park in a rural location midway between Falmouth and Helston. Its well-sheltered grassy pitches make this an ideal location for visiting the lovely beaches and towns nearby. An 8 acre site with 24 touring pitches and 23 statics.

Leisure:

Facilities:

Services:

Within 3 miles:

Notes: No pets, no disposable BBQs, no open fires. Free use of fridge/freezer in laundry room

FALMOUTH

►►► 74% Pennance Mill Farm Touring Park

Maenporth TR11 5HJ

☎ 01326 317431 01326 317431

dir: *From A39 (Truro to Falmouth road) follow brown camping signs towards Maenporth Beach. At Hill Head rdbt take 2nd exit for Maenporth Beach*

Open Etr-Xmas Last arrival 22.00hrs Last departure 10.00hrs

Set approximately half a mile from the safe, sandy bay at Maenporth, this is a mainly level, grassy park in a rural location sheltered by mature trees and shrubs and divided into three meadows. It has a modern toilet block. A 6 acre site with 75 touring pitches, 8 hardstandings and 4 statics.

Leisure:

Facilities:

Services:

Within 3 miles:

Notes: 0.5m private path to walk or cycle to beach

GOONHAVERN

►►►► 80% Silverbow Park

Perranwell TR4 9NX

☎ 01872 572347

dir: *Adjacent to A3075, 0.5m S of village*

Open May-mid Sep Last arrival 22.00hrs Last departure 10.30hrs

This park has a quiet garden atmosphere, and appeals to families with young children. The landscaped grounds and good quality toilet facilities, including four family rooms, are maintained to a very high standard with attention paid to detail. 9 seasonal touring pitches available. A 14 acre site with 100 touring pitches, 2 hardstandings and 15 statics.

Leisure:

Facilities:

Services:

Within 3 miles:

Notes: No cycling, no skateboards. Short mat bowls rink, conservation/information area

GOONHAVERN

►►► 75% Roseville Holiday Park

TR4 9LA

☎ 01872 572448 01872 572448

dir: *From mini-rdbt in Goonhavern follow B3285 towards Perranporth, site 0.5m on right*

Open Whit-Oct (rs Apr-Jul, Sep-Oct shop closed) Last arrival 21.30hrs Last departure 11.00hrs

A family park set in a rural location with sheltered grassy pitches, some gently sloping. The toilet facilities are modern, and there is an attractive outdoor swimming pool complex. Approximately two miles from the long sandy beach at Perranporth. An 8 acre site with 95 touring pitches and 5 statics.

Leisure:

Facilities:

Services:

Within 3 miles:

Notes: Families only. Off-licence in shop

GORRAN

►►► 80% Treveague Farm Caravan & Camping Site

PL26 6NY

☎ 01726 842295 📠 01726 842295

e-mail: treveague@btconnect.com

web: www.treveaguefarm.co.uk

dir: *From St Austell take B3273 towards Mevagissey, past Pentewan at top of hill, turn right signed Gorran. Past Heligan Gardens towards Gorran Churchtown. Follow brown tourist signs from fork in road*

* £7.50-£18 £7.50-£18 £6-£15

Open Apr-Oct Last arrival 21.00hrs Last departure noon

Spectacular coastal views can be enjoyed from this rural park, which is well equipped with modern facilities. A stone-faced toilet block with a Cornish slate roof is an attractive feature, as is the new building that houses the reception, shop and café. A footpath leads to the village of Gorran Haven one way, and the secluded sandy Vault Beach in the other. A 4 acre site with 40 touring pitches.

Leisure: Facilities: Services: Within 3 miles: Notes: Bird hide with observation cameras

HAYLE

78% St Ives Bay Holiday Park

73 Loggans Rd, Upton Towans TR27 5BH

☎ 01736 752274 📠 01736 754523

e-mail: stivesbay@btconnect.com

web: www.stivesbay.co.uk

dir: *Exit A30 at Hayle then immediate right onto B3301 at mini-rdbts. Site entrance 0.5m on left*

* £10-£31 £10-£31 £10-£31

Open Etr-1 Oct Last arrival 23.00hrs Last departure 09.00hrs

An extremely well maintained holiday park with a relaxed atmosphere, built on sand dunes adjacent to a three mile beach. The touring section forms a number of separate locations around this extensive park which is especially geared for families and couples. As well as the large indoor swimming pool there are two pubs with seasonal entertainment.
A 90 acre site with 240 touring pitches and 250 statics.

Leisure:

Facilities:

Services:

Within 3 miles: Notes: No pets. Crazy golf, video room. Wi-fi

HAYLE

►►► 78% Atlantic Coast Caravan Park

53 Upton Towans, Gwithian TR27 5BL

☎ 01736 752071 01736 758100

e-mail: enquiries@atlanticcoastpark.co.uk

dir: *From A30 into Hayle, turn right at double rdbt. Site 1.5m on left*

Open Mar-early Jan Last arrival 20.00hrs Last departure 11.00hrs

Fringed by the sand-dunes of St Ives Bay and close to the golden sands of Gwithian Beach, the small, friendly touring area offers fully serviced pitches. There's freshly baked bread, a takeaway and a bar next door. This park is ideally situated for visitors to enjoy the natural coastal beauty and attractions of south-west Cornwall. Static caravans for holiday hire and 8 seasonal touring pitches available. A 4.5 acre site with 15 touring pitches and 50 statics.

Facilities:

Services:

Within 3 miles:

Notes: No commercial vehicles, gazebos or day tents. Wi-fi

HAYLE

►►► 74% Treglisson Touring Park

Wheal Alfred Rd TR27 5JT

☎ 01736 753141

e-mail: enquiries@treglisson.co.uk

dir: *4th exit off rdbt on A30 at Hayle. 100mtrs, left at 1st mini-rdbt. 1.5km past golf course, site sign on left*

* £9.50-£16 £9.50-£16 £9.50-£16

Open Etr-Sep Last arrival 20.00hrs Last departure 11.00hrs

A small secluded site in a peaceful wooded meadow and a former apple and pear orchard. This quiet rural site has level grass pitches and a well-planned modern toilet block, and is just two miles from the glorious beach at Hayle with its vast stretch of golden sand. A 3 acre site with 26 touring pitches, 3 hardstandings.

Leisure:

Facilities:

Services:

Within 3 miles:

Notes: Max 6 people to one pitch, dogs must be on leads at all times. Tourist information, milk deliveries

HAYLE

►►► 70% Parbola Holiday Park

Wall, Gwinear TR27 5LE

☎ 01209 831503

e-mail: bookings@parbola.co.uk

dir: *At Hayle rdbt on A30 take Connor Downs exit. In 1m turn right signed Carnhell Green. In village right to Wall. Site in village on left*

* £12-£20.50 £12-£20.50 £12-£20.50

Open all year (rs Etr-end of Jun & Sep shop closed, unheated pool) Last arrival 21.00hrs Last departure 10.00hrs

Pitches are provided in both woodland and open areas in this spacious park in Cornish downland. The park is centrally located for touring the seaside resorts and towns in the area, especially nearby Hayle with its three miles of golden sands. 10 seasonal touring pitches available. A 16.5 acre site with 110 touring pitches, 4 hardstandings and 28 statics.

Leisure: **Facilities:** **Services:** **Within 3 miles:** **Notes:** Dogs not allowed Jul-Aug. Crazy golf & table tennis, giant chess & draughts, hairdressing, make-up room

HELSTON

►►► 77% Lower Polladras Touring Park

Carleen, Breage TR13 9NX

☎ 01736 762220 01736 762220

e-mail: lowerpolladras@btinternet.com

web: www.lower-polladras.co.uk

dir: *From Helston take A394 then B3302 (Hayle road) at Ward Garage, 2nd left to Carleen, site 2m on right*

Open Apr-Jan Last arrival 22.00hrs Last departure noon

A rural park with extensive views of surrounding fields, appealing to families who enjoy the countryside. The planted trees and shrubs are maturing, and help to divide the area into paddocks with spacious grassy pitches. A 4 acre site with 57 touring pitches, 23 hardstandings and 3 statics.

Leisure:

Facilities:

Services:

Within 3 miles:

Notes: Caravan & boat storage area. Wi-fi

HOLYWELL BAY

93% Trevornick Holiday Park

TR8 5PW

☎ 01637 830531 🖹 01637 831000

e-mail: info@trevornick.co.uk

web: www.trevornick.co.uk

dir: *3m from Newquay off A3075 towards Redruth. Follow Cubert & Holywell Bay signs*

Open Etr & mid May-mid Sep Last arrival 21.00hrs Last departure 10.00hrs

A large seaside holiday complex with excellent facilities and amenities. There is plenty of entertainment including a children's club and an evening cabaret, adding up to a full holiday experience for all the family. A sandy beach is just a 15-minute footpath walk away. The park has 68 ready-erected tents for hire. A 20 acre site with 593 touring pitches, 6 hardstandings.

Leisure:

Facilities:

Services:

Within 3 miles:

Notes: Families & couples only. Fishing, golf course, entertainment

HOLYWELL BAY

75% Holywell Bay Holiday Park

TR8 5PR

☎ 0844 335 3756 🖹 01637 831166

e-mail: touringandcamping@parkdeanholidays.com

web: www.parkdeantouring.com

dir: *Exit A30 onto A392, take A3075 signed Redruth, right in 2m signed Holywell/Cubert. Through Cubert past Trevornick to site on left*

* £10-£37 £10-£37 £10-£37

Open Mar-Oct (rs May-20 Sep pool open) Last arrival 21.00hrs Last departure 10.00hrs

Close to lovely beaches in a rural location, this level grassy park borders on National Trust land, and is close to the Cornish Coastal Path. The park provides a popular entertainment programme for the whole family (including evening entertainment), and there is an outdoor pool with a waterslide and children's clubs. Newquay is a few miles away. A 40 acre site with 40 touring pitches and 162 statics.

Leisure: **Facilities:** **Services:** **Within 3 miles:** **Notes:** No pets. Family entertainment, children's clubs, surf school & hire shop, adventure playground

KENNACK SANDS

►►► 76% Chy Carne Holiday Park

Kuggar, Ruan Minor TR12 7LX

☎ 01326 290200 & 291161

e-mail: enquiries@camping-cornwall.com

web: www.camping-cornwall.com

dir: *From A3083 turn left on B3293 after Culdrose Naval Air Station. At Goonhilly ESS right onto unclass road signed Kennack Sands. Left in 3m at junct*

Open Etr-Oct Last arrival dusk

A small but spacious park in a quiet, sheltered spot with extensive sea and coastal views from the grassy touring area. A village pub with restaurant is a short walk by footpath from the touring area, and a sandy beach is less than half a mile away. A 12 acre site with 30 touring pitches, 4 hardstandings and 18 statics.

Leisure:

Facilities:

Services:

Within 3 miles:

Notes: Wi-fi

LANDRAKE

►►►► 81% Dolbeare Park Caravan and Camping

St Ive Rd PL12 5AF

☎ 01752 851332 01752 547871

e-mail: reception@dolbeare.co.uk

web: www.dolbeare.co.uk

dir: *A38 to Landrake, 4m W of Saltash. At footbridge over A38 turn right, follow signs to site (0.75m from A38)*

Open all year Last arrival 18.00hrs Last departure noon

A mainly level grass site with trees and bushes set in meadowland. The keen and friendly owners set high standards, and the park is always neat and clean. The refurbished toilet block with its new inviting interior and spacious family rooms is particularly impressive. A 9 acre site with 60 touring pitches, 54 hardstandings.

Leisure:

Facilities:

Services:

Within 3 miles:

Notes: No cycling, no kite flying, dogs must be kept on leads. Info centre, off licence, free fridge & freezer. Wi-fi

LANIVET

►►► 78% Mena Caravan & Camping Park

PL30 5HW

☎ 01208 831845 🖷 01208 831845

e-mail: mena@campsitesincornwall.co.uk

dir: *Exit A30 onto A389 N signed Lanivet & Bodmin. In 0.5m 1st right & pass under A30. 1st left signed Lostwithiel & Fowey. In 0.25m right at top of hill. 0.5m then 1st right. Entrance 100yds on right*

Open all year Last arrival 22.00hrs Last departure noon

Set in a secluded, elevated location with high hedges for shelter, and plenty of peace. This grassy site is about four miles from the Eden Project and midway between the north and south Cornish coasts. There is a small coarse fishing lake on site and two static caravans for holiday hire. A 15 acre site with 25 touring pitches, 1 hardstandings and 2 statics.

Leisure:
Facilities:
Services:
Within 3 miles:

LEEDSTOWN (NEAR HAYLE)

►►►► 74% Calloose Caravan & Camping Park

TR27 5ET

☎ 01736 850431 & 0800 328 7589

🖷 01736 850431

e-mail: calloose@hotmail.com

dir: *From Hayle take B3302 to Leedstown, turn left opposite village hall, before entering village. Site 0.5m on left at bottom of hill*

Open Mar-Nov, Xmas & New Year (rs Mar-mid May & late Sep-Nov swimming pool closed) Last arrival 22.00hrs Last departure 11.00hrs

A comprehensively equipped leisure park in a remote rural setting in a small river valley. This very good park is busy and bustling, and offers bright and clean facilities. There are log cabins and static caravans for holiday hire, and 18 seasonal touring pitches are available. A 12.5 acre site with 109 touring pitches, 29 hardstandings and 25 statics.

Leisure:
Facilities:
Services:
Within 3 miles:
Notes: Crazy golf, skittle alley

LOOE

68% Tencreek Holiday Park

Polperro Rd PL13 2JR

☎ 01503 262447 01503 262760

e-mail: reception@tencreek.co.uk

web: www.dolphinholidays.co.uk

dir: *Take A387 1.25m from Looe. Site on left*

* £9.50-£18.90 £9.50-£18.90 £9.50-£18.90

Open all year Last arrival 23.00hrs Last departure 10.00hrs

Occupying a lovely position with extensive countryside and sea views, this holiday centre is in a rural spot but close to Looe and Polperro. There is a full family entertainment programme, with indoor and outdoor swimming pools, an adventure playground and an exciting children's club. A 24 acre site with 254 touring pitches and 101 statics.

Leisure:

Facilities:

Services:

Within 3 miles:

Notes: Families & couples only. Nightly entertainment, solarium, 45-metre pool flume

LOOE

►►►► 75% Tregoad Park

St Martin PL13 1PB

☎ 01503 262718 01503 264777

e-mail: info@tregoadpark.co.uk

web: www.tregoadpark.co.uk

dir: *Signed with direct access from B3253, or from E on A387 follow B3253 for 1.75m towards Looe. Site on left*

Open all year Last arrival 20.00hrs Last departure 11.00hrs

A smart, terraced park with extensive sea and rural views, about 1.5 miles from Looe. All pitches are level, the facilities are well maintained, and there is a licensed bar with bar meals served in the conservatory. American trailers, static caravans, holiday cottages and two camping pods for holiday hire. A 55 acre site with 200 touring pitches, 60 hardstandings and 3 statics.

Leisure:

Facilities:

Services:

Within 3 miles:

Notes: Fishing lake, crazy golf, ball sports area. Wi-fi

LOOE

►►► 85% Camping Caradon Touring Park

Trelawne PL13 2NA

☎ 01503 272388 📠 01503 272858

e-mail: enquiries@campingcaradon.co.uk

dir: *Site signed from B3359 near junct with A387, between Looe & Polperro*

* £10-£19.50 £10-£19.50 £10-£19.50

Open all year (rs Nov-Mar by booking only) Last arrival 22.00hrs Last departure noon

Set in a quiet rural location between the popular coastal resorts of Looe and Polperro, this family-run park is just 1.5 miles from the beach at Talland Bay. The owners have upgraded the bar and restaurant, and are continuing to improve the park. A 3.5 acre site with 85 touring pitches, 23 hardstandings.

Leisure:

Facilities:

Services:

Within 3 miles:

Notes: Level site with good access

LOOE

►►► 77% Polborder House Caravan & Camping Park

Bucklawren Rd, St Martin PL13 1NZ

☎ 01503 240265

e-mail: reception@peaceful-polborder.co.uk

dir: *Approach Looe from E on A387, follow B3253 for 1m, left at Polborder & Monkey Sanctuary sign. Site 0.5m on right*

Open all year Last arrival 22.00hrs Last departure 11.00hrs

A very neat and well-kept small grassy site on high ground above Looe in a peaceful rural setting. Friendly and enthusiastic owners. A 3.3 acre site with 31 touring pitches, 18 hardstandings and 5 statics.

Leisure:

Facilities:

Services:

Within 3 miles:

Notes: Dogs allowed but no exercise area. Washing/food prep sinks, information centre. Wi-fi

LOSTWITHIEL

►►►► 78% Eden Valley Holiday Park

PL30 5BU

☎ 01208 872277 01208 871236

e-mail: enquiries@edenvalleyholidaypark.co.uk

dir: *1.5m SW of Lostwithiel on A390 turn right at brown/white sign in 400mtrs*

* £11-£15 £11-£15 £11-£15

Open Etr or Apr-Oct Last arrival 22.00hrs Last departure 11.30hrs

A grassy park set in attractive paddocks with mature trees. The gradual upgrading of facilities continues, and both buildings and grounds are carefully maintained. This park is ideally located for visiting the Eden Project, the nearby golden beaches and sailing at Fowey. Two self-catering lodges and 20 seasonal touring pitches are available. A 12 acre site with 56 touring pitches, 12 hardstandings and 38 statics.

Leisure:

Facilities:

Services:

Within 3 miles:

Notes: Badminton, soft tennis, putting green

LUXULYAN

►►► 77% Croft Farm Holiday Park

PL30 5EQ

☎ 01726 850228 01726 850498

e-mail: enquiries@croftfarm.co.uk

dir: *Exit A30 at Bodmin onto A391 towards St Austell. In 7m left at double rdbt onto unclass road towards Luxulyan/Eden Project, continue to rdbt at Eden, left signed Luxulyan. Site 1m on left. (NB Do not approach any other way as roads are very narrow)*

* £10.50-£15.50 £10.50-£15.50 £10.50-£15.50

Open 21 Mar-21 Jan Last arrival 18.00hrs Last departure 11.00hrs

A peaceful, picturesque setting at the edge of a wooded valley, and only one mile from The Eden Project. A 10.5 acre site with 52 touring pitches, 20 hardstandings and 40 statics.

Leisure:

Facilities:

Services:

Within 3 miles:

Notes: No skateboarding, ball games only on playing field, quiet between 23.00hrs-07.00hrs. Woodland walk, crazy golf, information room

MARAZION

►►► 76% Wheal Rodney Holiday Park

Gwallon Ln TR17 0HL

☎ 01736 710605

e-mail: reception@whealrodney.co.uk

dir: *Exit A30 at Crowlas, signed Rospeath. Site 1.5m on right. From Marazion centre turn opposite Fire Engine Inn, site 500mtrs on left*

* £14-£18 £14-£18 £10-£15

Open Etr-Oct Last arrival 20.00hrs Last departure 11.00hrs

Set in a quiet rural location surrounded by farmland, with level grass pitches and well-kept facilities. Just half a mile away are the beach at Marazion and the causeway and the ferry to St Michael's Mount. A cycle route is just 400 yards away. A 2.5 acre site with 30 touring pitches.

Leisure:

Facilities:

Services:

Within 3 miles:

Notes: Quiet after 22.00hrs. Wi-fi

MAWGAN PORTH

►►►► 77% Sun Haven Valley Holiday Park

TR8 4BQ

☎ 01637 860373 01637 860373

e-mail: sunhaven@sunhavenvalley.com

dir: *Exit A30 at Highgate Hill junct for Newquay; follow signs for airport. At T-junct turn right. At beach level in Mawgan Porth take only road inland, then 0.25m. Site 0.5m beyond S bend*

Open Apr-Oct Last arrival 22.00hrs Last departure 10.30hrs

An attractive site with level pitches on the side of a river valley. The very high quality facilities include a TV lounge and a games room in a Swedish-style chalet, and a well-kept adventure playground. Trees and hedges fringe the park, and the ground is well drained. A 5 acre site with 109 touring pitches and 38 statics.

Leisure:

Facilities:

Services:

Within 3 miles:

Notes: Families & couples only. Wi-fi

MAWGAN PORTH

►►► 79% Trevarrian Holiday Park

TR8 4AQ

☎ 01637 860381 & 0845 2255910

e-mail: holiday@trevarrian.co.uk

dir: *From A39 at St Columb rdbt turn right onto A3059 towards Newquay. Fork right in approx 2m for St Mawgan onto B3276. Turn right, site on left*

Open Etr-Sep Last arrival 22.00hrs Last departure 11.00hrs

A well-established and well-run holiday park overlooking Mawgan Porth beach. This park has a wide range of attractions including a free entertainment programme in peak season. 10 seasonal touring pitches available. A 7 acre site with 185 touring pitches.

Leisure:

Facilities:

Services:

Within 3 miles:

Notes: Sports field, pitch 'n' putt

MEVAGISSEY

►►►►► 96% Seaview International Holiday Park

Boswinger PL26 6LL

☎ 01726 843425 01726 843358

e-mail: holidays@seaviewinternational.com

web: www.seaviewinternational.com

dir: *From St Austell take B3273 signed Mevagissey. Turn right before entering village. Follow brown tourist signs to site*

Open Mar-Oct Last arrival 21.00hrs Last departure 10.00hrs

An attractive holiday park overlooking Veryan Bay, with colourful landscaping, Seaview continues to offer an outstanding holiday experience, with luxury family pitches, super toilet facilities, takeaway and shop, and 38 static caravans for hire. The beach and sea are half a mile away. A 28 acre site with 189 touring pitches, 13 hardstandings and 38 statics.

Leisure: Facilities: Services: Within 3 miles: Notes: Restrictions on certain dog breeds. Crazy golf, volleyball, badminton, tennis & scuba diving.

MULLION

74% Mullion Holiday Park

Ruan Minor TR12 7LJ

0844 335 3756 01326 241141

e-mail: touringandcamping@parkdeanholidays.com

web: www.parkdeantouring.com

dir: *A30 onto A39 through Truro towards Falmouth. A394 to Helston, A3083 for The Lizard. Site 7m on left*

* £9-£36 £9-£36 £9-£36

Open Apr-Oct (rs 17 May-20 Sep outdoor pool open) Last arrival 22.00hrs Last departure 10.00hrs

A comprehensively-equipped leisure park geared mainly for self-catering holidays, and set close to the sandy beaches, coves and fishing villages on The Lizard peninsula. There is plenty of on-site entertainment for all ages, with indoor and outdoor swimming pools and a bar and grill. A 49 acre site with 150 touring pitches, 8 hardstandings and 305 statics.

Leisure: **Facilities:** **Services:** **Within 3 miles:**

Notes: Family site. Scuba diving, football pitch, multi-sports court, surf & cycle hire. Wi-fi

NEWQUAY

82% Hendra Holiday Park

TR8 4NY

01637 875778 01637 879017

e-mail: enquiries@hendra-holidays.com

dir: *A30 onto A392 signed Newquay. At Quintrell Downs over rdbt, signed Lane, site 0.5m on left*

Open Apr-Oct (rs Apr-Spring BH, Sep-Oct outdoor pool closed) Last arrival dusk Last departure 10.00hrs

A large complex with holiday statics and superb facilities including an indoor fun pool and an outdoor pool. There is a children's club for the over 6s, and evening entertainment during high season. The touring pitches are set amongst mature trees and shrubs, and some have fully-serviced facilities. All amenities are open to the public. An 80 acre site with 548 touring pitches, 28 hardstandings and 283 statics.

Leisure:

Facilities:

Services:

Within 3 miles:

Notes: Families & couples only. Solarium, fish bar, train rides

NEWQUAY

75% Newquay Holiday Park

TR8 4HS

☎ 0844 335 3756 🖹 01637 850818

e-mail: touringandcamping@parkdeanholidays.com

web: www.parkdeantouring.com

dir: *From Bodmin on A30, under low bridge, right towards RAF St Mawgan. Take A3059 towards Newquay, site past Treloy Golf Club*

* £12-£39 £12-£39 £12-£39

Open Mar-Oct (rs May-20 Sep pool open) Last arrival 21.00hrs Last departure 10.00hrs

A well-maintained park with a wide range of indoor and outdoor activities. A children's playground and bar and grill enhance the facilities, and the club and bars offer quality entertainment. Three heated outdoor pools and a giant waterslide are very popular. A 60 acre site with 50 touring pitches, 10 hardstandings and 262 statics.

Leisure:

Facilities:

Services:

Within 3 miles:

Notes: Pool room, family entertainment, children's clubs. Wi-fi

NEWQUAY

►►►► 75% Trencreek Holiday Park

Hillcrest, Higher Trencreek TR8 4NS

☎ 01637 874210 🖹 01637 874210

e-mail: trencreek@btconnect.com

dir: *A392 to Quintrell Downs, right towards Newquay, left at 2 mini-rdbts into Trevenson Rd to site*

* £10.20-£16.60 £10.20-£16.60 £10.20-£16.60

Open Whit-mid Sep Last arrival 22.00hrs Last departure noon

An attractively landscaped park in the village of Trencreek, with modern toilet facilities of a very high standard. Two well-stocked fishing lakes, and evening entertainment in the licensed clubhouse are extra draws. Located about two miles from Newquay with its beaches and surfing. A 10 acre site with 194 touring pitches, 8 hardstandings and 6 statics.

Leisure:

Facilities:

Services:

Within 3 miles:

Notes: Families & couples only. Free coarse fishing on site

NEWQUAY

►►► 81% Treloy Touring Park

TR8 4JN

☎ 01637 872063 & 876279

01637 872063

e-mail: treloy.tp@btconnect.com

web: www.treloy.co.uk

dir: *Off A3059 (St Columb Major-Newquay road)*

fr £12 fr £12 fr £12

Open May-15 Sep (rs Sep pool, takeaway, shop & bar) Last arrival 21.00hrs Last departure 10.00hrs

Attractive site with fine countryside views, within easy reach of resorts and beaches. The pitches are set in four paddocks with mainly level but some slightly sloping grassy areas. Maintenance and cleanliness are very high. An 18 acre site with 223 touring pitches, 24 hardstandings.

Leisure:

Facilities:

Services:

Within 3 miles:

Notes: Entertainment, concessionary green fees for golf. Wi-fi

NEWQUAY

►►► 77% Trethiggey Touring Park

Quintrell Downs TR8 4QR

☎ 01637 877672 01637 879706

e-mail: enquiries@trethiggey.co.uk

dir: *A30 onto A392 signed Newquay at Quintrell Downs rdbt, left onto A3058, pass Newquay Pearl centre. Site 0.5m on left*

Open Mar-Dec Last arrival 22.00hrs Last departure 10.30hrs

A family-owned park in a rural setting that is ideal for touring this part of Cornwall. Pleasantly divided into paddocks with maturing trees and shrubs, and offering coarse fishing and tackle hire. A 15 acre site with 145 touring pitches, 35 hardstandings and 12 statics.

Leisure:

Facilities:

Services:

Within 3 miles:

Notes: Off licence, recreation field, fishing. Wi-fi

NEWQUAY

►►► 76% Trebellan Park

Cubert TR8 5PY

☎ 01637 830522 01637 830277

e-mail: enquiries@trebellan.co.uk

dir: *4m S of Newquay, turn W off A3075 at Cubert sign. Left in 0.75m onto unclass road*

* £16-£24 £16-£24 £12-£20

Open May-Oct Last arrival 21.00hrs Last departure 10.00hrs

A terraced grassy rural park within a picturesque valley with views of Cubert Common, and adjacent to the Smuggler's Den, a 16th-century thatched inn. This park has three well-stocked coarse fishing lakes on site. An 8 acre site with 150 touring pitches and 7 statics.

Leisure:

Facilities:

Services:

Within 3 miles:

Notes: Families & couples only

NEWQUAY

►►► 74% Riverside Holiday Park

Gwills Ln TR8 4PE

☎ 01637 873617 01637 877051

e-mail: info@riversideholidaypark.co.uk

web: www.riversideholidaypark.co.uk

dir: *A30 onto A392 signed Newquay. At Quintrell Downs cross rdbt signed Lane. 2nd left in 0.5m onto unclass road signed Gwills. Site in 400yds*

* £10-£14 £10-£14 £10-£14

Open Mar-Oct Last arrival 22.00hrs Last departure 10.00hrs

A sheltered valley beside a river in a quiet location is the idyllic setting for this lightly wooded park which caters for families and couples only. The fairly simple facilities continue to be upgraded. The site is close to the wide variety of attractions offered by the major resort of Newquay, and it has self-catering lodges, cabins and static vans for hire. An 11 acre site with 65 touring pitches and 65 statics.

Leisure:

Facilities:

Services:

Within 3 miles:

Notes: Families and couples only

NEWQUAY

►►► 74% Trenance Holiday Park

Edgcumbe Av TR7 2JY

☎ 01637 873447 01637 852677

e-mail: enquiries@trenanceholidaypark.co.uk

dir: *Off A3075 near viaduct. Site by boating lake rdbt*

* £14-£18 £14-£18

Open 26 May-Oct Last arrival 22.00hrs Last departure 10.00hrs

A mainly static park popular with tenters, close to Newquay's vibrant nightlife, and serving excellent breakfasts and takeaways. Set on high ground in an urban area of town, with cheerful owners and clean facilities. A 12 acre site with 50 touring pitches and 190 statics.

Leisure:

Facilities:

Services:

Within 3 miles:

Notes: No pets

OTTERHAM

►►► 77% St Tinney Farm Holidays

PL32 9TA

☎ 01840 261274

e-mail: info@st-tinney.co.uk

dir: *Signed 1m off A39 via unclass road signed Otterham*

£4.50-£8 £4.50-£8 £4.50-£8

Open Etr-Oct Last arrival 21.00hrs Last departure 10.00hrs

A family-run farm site in a rural area with nature trails, lakes, valleys and offering complete seclusion. Visitors are free to walk around the farmland lakes and lose themselves in the countryside. A 34 acre site with 20 touring pitches and 15 statics.

Leisure:

Facilities:

Services:

Within 3 miles:

Notes: Coarse fishing. Wi-fi

PADSTOW

►►►► 80% Padstow Touring Park

PL28 8LE

☎ 01841 532061

e-mail: mail@padstowtouringpark.co.uk

dir: *1m S of Padstow, on E side of A389 (Padstow to Wadebridge road)*

* £10-£15.50 £10-£15.50 £10-£15.50

Open all year Last arrival 21.30hrs Last departure 11.00hrs

A much upgraded park set in open countryside above the quaint fishing town of Padstow which can be approached by footpath directly from the park. It is divided into paddocks by maturing bushes and hedges to create a peaceful and relaxing holiday atmosphere. A 13.5 acre site with 100 touring pitches, 14 hardstandings.

Leisure:

Facilities:

Services:

Within 3 miles:

Notes: No groups. Wi-fi

PENTEWAN

82% Pentewan Sands Holiday Park

PL26 6BT

☎ 01726 843485 01726 844142

e-mail: info@pentewan.co.uk

dir: *On B3273 4m S of St Austell*

fr £13.95 fr £13.95 fr £13.95

Open Apr-Oct (rs Apr-14 May & 15 Sep-Oct some facilities closed) Last arrival 22.00hrs Last departure 10.30hrs

A large holiday park with a wide range of amenities, set on grassy pitches beside a private beach where plenty of aquatic activities are available. A short stroll leads to the pretty village of Pentewan, and other attractions are a short drive away. A club on site offers evening entertainment. A 32 acre site with 500 touring pitches and 120 statics.

Leisure:

Facilities:

Services:

Within 3 miles:

Notes: No jet skis. Cycles, boat launch, water sports, caravan store. Wi-fi

PENTEWAN

►►►►► 78% Sun Valley Holiday Park

Pentewan Rd PL26 6DJ

☎ 01726 843266 & 844393

01726 843266

e-mail: reception@sunvalley-holidays.co.uk

dir: *From St Austell take B3273 towards Mevagissey. Site 2m on right*

Open all year (rs Winter pool & restaurant) Last arrival 22.00hrs Last departure 10.30hrs

In a valley amongst woodland, this neat park is kept to a very high standard. Extensive amenities include tennis courts, indoor swimming pool, licensed clubhouse and restaurant. The sea is mile away, and can be accessed via a footpath and cycle path along the river bank. A 20 acre site with 29 touring pitches, 4 hardstandings and 75 statics.

Leisure: **Facilities:** **Services:** **Within 3 miles:**

Notes: Certain pet restrictions apply, please contact for details. No motorised scooters/ skateboards or bikes at night. Pets corner, bike hire, outdoor & indoor play areas

PENTEWAN

►►► 78% Heligan Woods

PL26 6BT

☎ 01726 842714 01726 844142

e-mail: info@pentewan.co.uk

dir: *From A390 take B3273 for Mevagissey at x-roads signed 'No caravans beyond this point'. Right onto unclass road towards Gorran, site 0.75m on left*

Open 16 Jan-26 Nov Last arrival 22.30hrs Last departure 10.30hrs

A pleasant peaceful park adjacent to the Lost Gardens of Heligan, with views over St Austell Bay, and well-maintained facilities. Guests can also use the extensive amenities at the sister park, Pentewan Sands, and there's a footpath with direct access to Heligan Gardens. A 12 acre site with 89 touring pitches and 30 statics.

Leisure:

Facilities:

Services:

Within 3 miles:

PERRANPORTH

76% Perran Sands Holiday Park

TR6 0AQ

☎ 01872 573511 🖹 01872 571158

e-mail: nick.cooke@bourne-leisure.co.uk

dir: *A30 onto B3285 towards Perranporth. Site on right before descent on hill into Perranporth*

* £12-£111 £12-£111 £12-£64

Open mid Mar-Oct (rs mid Mar-May & Sep-Oct some facilities may be reduced) Last arrival 22.00hrs Last departure 10.00hrs

Nestling amid 500 acres of protected dune grassland, and with a footpath through to the surf and three miles of golden sandy beach, this lively park is set in a large village-style complex. It offers a complete range of on-site facilities and entertainment for all the family which makes it an extremely popular park. 25 seasonal touring pitches available. A 550 acre site with 360 touring pitches, 20 hardstandings and 600 statics.

Leisure:

Facilities:

Services:

Within 3 miles:

Notes: Families & couples only. Certain dog breeds are not accepted. Wi-fi

PERRANPORTH

►►► 85% Tollgate Farm Caravan & Camping Park

Budnick Hill TR6 0AD

☎ 01872 572130 & 0845 166 2126

e-mail: enquiries@tollgatefarm.co.uk

dir: *Off A30 onto B3285 to Perranporth. Site on right 1.5m after Goonhavern*

Open Etr-Sep Last arrival 21.00hrs Last departure 11.00hrs

A quiet site in a rural location with spectacular coastal views. Pitches are divided into four paddocks sheltered and screened by mature hedges. Children will enjoy the play equipment and pets' corner. The three miles of sand at Perran Bay are just a walk away through the sand dunes, or a 0.75 mile drive. A 10 acre site with 102 touring pitches, 10 hardstandings.

Leisure:

Facilities:

Services:

Within 3 miles:

Notes: No large groups. Family shower rooms with baby changing facilities available. Wi-fi

PERRANPORTH

►►► 69% Perranporth Camping & Touring Park

Budnick Rd TR6 0DB

☎ 01872 572174 Fax 01872 572174

dir: *0.5m E off B3285*

* £15-£20 £15-£20 £15-£20

Open Whit-Sep (rs Etr & end Sep shop & club facilities closed) Last arrival 23.00hrs Last departure noon

A mainly tenting site with few level pitches, located high above a fine sandy beach which is much-frequented by surfers. The park is attractive to young people, and is set in a lively town on a spectacular part of the coast. 9 static caravans for holiday hire. A 6 acre site with 120 touring pitches, 4 hardstandings and 9 statics.

Leisure:

Facilities:

Services:

Within 3 miles:

Notes: All dogs on leads, no noise after 23.00hrs

POLRUAN

►►► 81% Polruan Holidays-Camping & Caravanning

Polruan-by-Fowey PL23 1QH

☎ 01726 870263

e-mail: polholiday@aol.com

web: www.polruanholidays.co.uk

dir: *A38 to Dobwalls, left onto A390 to East Taphouse. Left onto B3359. Right in 4.5m signed Polruan*

Open Etr-Oct Last arrival 21.00hrs Last departure noon

A very rural and quiet site in a lovely elevated position above the village, with good views of the sea. The River Fowey passenger ferry is close by, and the site has a good shop, and barbecues to borrow. A 3 acre site with 47 touring pitches, 7 hardstandings and 10 statics.

Leisure:

Facilities:

Services:

Within 3 miles:

Notes: No skateboards, roller skates, bikes, water pistols or water bombs. Tourist information

PORTHTOWAN

►►►► 82% Porthtowan Tourist Park

Mile Hill TR4 8TY

☎ 01209 890256

e-mail: admin@porthtowantouristpark.co.uk

web: www.porthtowantouristpark.co.uk

dir: *Exit A30 at junct signed Redruth/ Porthtowan. Take 3rd exit at rdbt. 2m, right at T-junct. Site on left at top of hill*

* £9.50-£16 £9.50-£16 £9.50-£16

Open Apr-Sep Last arrival 21.30hrs Last departure 11.00hrs

A neat, level grassy site on high ground above Porthtowan, with plenty of shelter from mature trees and shrubs. The superb toilet facilities considerably enhance the appeal of this peaceful rural park, which is almost midway between the small seaside resorts of Portreath and Porthtowan, with their beaches and surfing. A 5 acre site with 80 touring pitches, 2 hardstandings.

Leisure:

Facilities:

Services:

Within 3 miles:

Notes: No bikes/skateboards during Jul-Aug

PORTHTOWAN

►►► 79% Wheal Rose Caravan & Camping Park

Wheal Rose TR16 5DD

☎ 01209 891496

e-mail: les@whealrosecaravanpark.co.uk

dir: *Exit A30 at Scorrier sign, follow signs to Wheal Rose. Site 0.5m on left (Wheal Rose to Porthtowan road)*

* £10-£16 £10-£16 £10-£16

Open Mar-Dec Last arrival 21.00hrs Last departure 11.00hrs

A quiet, peaceful park in a secluded valley setting, central for beaches and countryside, and two miles from the surfing beaches of Porthtowan. The friendly owners work hard to keep this park immaculate, with a bright toilet block and well-trimmed pitches. A 6 acre site with 50 touring pitches, 6 hardstandings and 3 statics.

Leisure:

Facilities:

Services:

Within 3 miles:

Notes: 5mph speed limit, dogs on leads, minimum noise after 23.00hrs, gates locked at 23.00hrs. Family bathroom

PORTREATH

►►► 82% Tehidy Holiday Park

Harris Mill, Illogan TR16 4JQ

☎ 01209 216489 📠 01209 216489

e-mail: holiday@tehidy.co.uk

web: www.tehidy.co.uk

dir: *Exit A30 at Redruth/Portreath junct onto A3047 to 1st rdbt. Left onto B3300. At junct straight over signed Tehidy Holiday Park. Past Cornish Arms pub, 800yds bottom of hill on left*

* £10-£16 £10-£16 £10-£16

Open Apr-Oct Last arrival 20.00hrs Last departure 10.00hrs

An attractive wooded location in a quiet rural area only 2.5 miles from popular beaches. Mostly level pitches on tiered ground, and the toilet facilities are bright and modern. Holiday static caravans for hire and 6 seasonal touring pitches available. A 4.5 acre site with 18 touring pitches, 11 hardstandings and 32 statics.

Leisure:

Facilities:

Services:

Within 3 miles:

Notes: Trampoline, off-licence. Wi-fi

REDRUTH

►►►► 79% Globe Vale Holiday Park

Radnor TR16 4BH

☎ 01209 891183 📠 01209 890590

e-mail: info@globevale.co.uk

dir: *A30 take Redruth/Porthtowan exit then Portreath/North Country exit from rdbt, right at x-rds into Radnor Rd, left after 0.5m, site on left after 0.5m*

* £8-£20 £10-£20 £8-£18

Open Etr-Oct Last arrival 20.00hrs Last departure 10.00hrs

A family owned and run park set in a quiet rural location yet close to some stunning beaches and coastline. The park has a newly created touring area with a number of full-facility hardstanding pitches, a toilet block with a new family room and a comfortable lounge bar. 4 holiday static caravans for hire. A 13 acre site with 77 touring pitches, 19 hardstandings and 4 statics.

Leisure:

Facilities:

Services:

Within 3 miles:

Notes: Pets must be kept on leads throughout the park

REDRUTH

▶▶▶ 78% Lanyon Holiday Park

Loscombe Ln, Four Lanes TR16 6LP

☎ 01209 313474

e-mail: info@lanyonholidaypark.co.uk

web: www.lanyonholidaypark.co.uk

dir: *Signed 0.5m off B2397 on Helston side of Four Lanes village*

* £10-£18 £10-£18 £8-£16

Open Mar-Oct Last arrival 21.00hrs Last departure noon

Small, friendly rural park in an elevated position with fine views to distant St Ives Bay. This family owned and run park continues to be upgraded in all areas, with a new toilet block and two holiday lodges, and is close to a cycling trail. Stithian's Reservoir for fishing, sailing and windsurfing is two miles away. 20 static holiday caravans for hire. A 14 acre site with 25 touring pitches and 49 statics.

Leisure:

Facilities:

Services:

Within 3 miles:

Notes: Family park. Take-away service, all-day games room. Wi-fi

REDRUTH

▶▶▶ 75% Cambrose Touring Park

Portreath Rd TR16 4HT

☎ 01209 890747

e-mail: cambrosetouringpark@supanet.com

dir: *A30 onto B3300 towards Portreath. Approx 0.75m at 1st rdbt right onto B3300. Take unclass road on right signed Porthtowan. Site 200yds on left*

Open Apr-Oct Last arrival 22.00hrs Last departure 11.30hrs

Situated in a rural setting surrounded by trees and shrubs, this park is divided into grassy paddocks. About two miles from the harbour village of Portreath. A 6 acre site with 60 touring pitches.

Leisure:

Facilities:

Services:

Within 3 miles:

Notes: Mini football pitch, family shower room

REJERRAH

80% Monkey Tree Holiday Park

Scotland Rd TR8 5QR

☎ 01872 572032 01872 573577

e-mail: enquiries@monkeytreeholidaypark.co.uk

web: www.monkeytreeholidaypark.co.uk

dir: *Exit A30 onto B3285 to Perranporth, 0.25m right into Scotland Rd, site on left in 1.5m*

Open all year Last arrival 22.00hrs Last departure 10.00hrs

Busy holiday park with plenty of activities and jolly holiday atmosphere. Set close to beaches between Newquay and Perranporth, facilities include two bars with entertainment, and a choice of eating outlets including a restaurant and a takeaway. 145 seasonal touring pitches available. A 56 acre site with 505 touring pitches, 17 hardstandings and 48 statics.

Leisure: **Facilities:** **Services:** **Within 3 miles:**

Notes: Families & couples only. Sauna, solarium, bike hire, mini diggers, amusement arcade & aqua-blaster. Wi-fi

REJERRAH

►►►► 86% Newperran Holiday Park

TR8 5QJ

☎ 01872 572407 01872 571254

e-mail: holidays@newperran.co.uk

dir: *4m SE of Newquay & 1m S of Rejerrah on A3075. Or A30 Redruth, exit B3275 Perranporth, at 1st T-junct right onto A3075 towards Newquay, site 300mtrs on left*

* £13.20-£19.90 £13.20-£19.90 £13.20-£19.90

Open Etr-Oct Last arrival mdnt Last departure 10.00hrs

A family site in a rural position near several beaches and bays. This airy park offers screening to some pitches, which are set in paddocks on level ground. High season entertainment is available in the park's country inn, and the café has an extensive menu. A 25 acre site with 357 touring pitches, 14 hardstandings and 6 statics.

Leisure: **Facilities:** **Services:** **Within 3 miles:**

Notes: Families & couples only. No skateboards. Dogs must be kept on leads. Adventure playground

ROSUDGEON

►►► 79%

Kenneggy Cove Holiday Park

Higher Kenneggy TR20 9AU

☎ 01736 763453

e-mail: enquiries@kenneggycove.co.uk

web: www.kenneggycove.co.uk

dir: *On A394 between Penzance & Helston, turn S into signed lane to site & Higher Kenneggy*

Open 17 May-4 Oct Last arrival 21.00hrs Last departure 11.00hrs

Set in an Area of Outstanding Natural Beauty with spectacular sea views, this family-owned park is quiet and well kept. A short walk along a country footpath leads to the Cornish coastal path, and on to the golden sandy beach at Kenneggy Cove. A 4 acre site with 50 touring pitches and 9 statics.

Leisure:

Facilities:

Services:

Within 3 miles:

Notes: No large groups. Fresh bakery items & homemade takeaway food

RUMFORD

►►► 80%

Music Water Touring Park

PL27 7SJ

☎ 01841 540257

dir: *A39 at Winnards Perch rdbt onto B3274 signed Padstow. Left in 2m onto unclass road signed Rumford & St Eval. Site 500mtrs on right*

* £9-£13 £9-£13 £9-£13

Open Apr-Oct Last arrival 23.00hrs Last departure 11.00hrs

Set in a peaceful location yet only a short drive to the pretty fishing town of Padstow, and many sandy beaches and coves. This family-owned and run park has grassy paddocks. There is a quiet lounge bar and a separate children's games room. A 8 acre site with 55 touring pitches, 2 hardstandings and 2 statics.

Leisure:

Facilities:

Services:

Within 3 miles:

Notes: Maximum 2 dogs per pitch & 1 tent per pitch. Pets corner (donkeys)

ST AUSTELL

►►►► 84% River Valley Holiday Park

London Apprentice PL26 7AP

01726 73533

e-mail: mail@cornwall-holidays.co.uk

web: www.cornwall-holidays.co.uk

dir: *Direct access to site signed on B3273 from St Austell at London Apprentice*

* £12.50-£25.50 £12.50-£25.50 £12.50-£25.50

Open end Mar-end Sep Last arrival 21.00hrs Last departure 11.00hrs

A neat, well-maintained family-run park set in a pleasant river valley. The quality toilet block and attractively landscaped grounds make this a delightful base for a holiday. A 2 acre site with 45 touring pitches, 45 hardstandings and 40 statics.

Leisure:

Facilities:

Services:

Within 3 miles:

Notes: Off-road cycle trail to beach. Wi-fi

ST AUSTELL

►►► 78% Court Farm Holidays

St Stephen PL26 7LE

01726 823684 01726 823684

e-mail: truscott@ctfarm.freeserve.co.uk

dir: *From St Austell take A3058 towards Newquay. Through St Stephen (pass Peugeot garage). Right at St Stephen/Coombe Hay/ Langreth/Industrial site sign. 400yds, site on right*

£12.50-£17.50 £12.50-£19.50 £9.50-£25

Open Apr-Sep Last arrival by dark Last departure 11.00hrs

Set in a peaceful rural location, this large camping field offers plenty of space, and is handy for the Eden Project and the Lost Gardens of Heligan. Coarse fishing and star-gazing facilities are among the attractions. A 4 acre site with 20 touring pitches, 5 hardstandings.

Leisure:

Facilities:

Services:

Within 3 miles:

Notes: No noisy behaviour after dark. Astronomy lectures, observatory, solar observatory. Wi-fi

ST AUSTELL

►►► 74% Trencreek Farm Country Holiday Park

Hewas Water PL26 7JG

☎ 01726 882540 01726 883254

e-mail: reception@trencreek.co.uk

dir: *From A390 4m SW of St Austell onto B3287. 1m, site on left*

Open Mar-Oct (rs Mar-May, Sep-Oct various restrictions apply) Last arrival 21.00hrs Last departure noon

Set in a rural area, this park is divided into paddocks with hedges and trees, and has coarse fishing lakes. There are organised activities for children indoors and out in the summer holidays, while at other times adult breaks are offered. There are animals in pens which children can enter. Self-catering lodges, static caravans and 9 bungalows are available. A 56 acre site with 108 touring pitches, 18 hardstandings and 7 statics.

Leisure: **Facilities:** **Services:** **Within 3 miles:** **Notes:** Under 15s must be accompanied by adult in & around pool. 4 coarse fishing lakes

ST COLUMB MAJOR

►►► 81% Southleigh Manor Naturist Park

TR9 6HY

☎ 01637 880938 01637 881108

e-mail: enquiries@southleigh-manor.com

dir: *Exit A30 at junct with A39 signed Wadebridge. At Highgate Hill rdbt take A39. At Halloon rdbt take A39. At Trekenning rdbt take 4th exit. Site 500mtrs on right*

Open Etr-Oct (rs Peak times shop open) Last arrival 20.00hrs Last departure 10.30hrs

A very well maintained naturist park in the heart of the Cornish countryside, catering for families and couples only. Seclusion and security are very well planned, and the lovely gardens provide a calm setting. There are two lodges for holiday hire. A 4 acre site with 50 touring pitches.

Leisure:

Facilities:

Services:

Within 3 miles:

Notes: Sauna, spa bath, pool table, putting green

ST IVES

►►►►► 87% Polmanter Tourist Park

Halsetown TR26 3LX

☎ 01736 795640

e-mail: reception@polmanter.com

dir: *Signed off B3311 at Halsetown*

Open Whit-10 Sep (rs Whit shop, pool, bar & takeaway food closed) Last arrival 21.00hrs Last departure 10.00hrs

A well-developed touring park on high ground, Polmanter offers high quality in all areas, from the immaculate modern toilet blocks to the outdoor swimming pool and hard tennis courts. Pitches are individually marked and sited in meadows, and the park has been tastefully landscaped. The fishing port and beaches of St Ives are just 1.5 miles away, and there is a bus service in high season. A 20 acre site with 240 touring pitches, 10 hardstandings.

Leisure: **Facilities:** **Services:** **Within 3 miles:**

Notes: No skateboards, roller blades or heelys. Putting, sports field, 7 family shower rooms. Wi-fi

ST IVES

►►►► 87% Ayr Holiday Park

TR26 1EJ

☎ 01736 795855 01736 798797

e-mail: recept@ayrholidaypark.co.uk

dir: *From A30 follow St Ives 'large vehicles' route via B3311 through Halsetown onto B3306. Site signed towards St Ives town centre*

Open all year Last arrival 22.00hrs Last departure 10.00hrs

A well-established park on a cliffside overlooking St Ives Bay, with a heated toilet block making winter holidaying more attractive. There are stunning views from most pitches, and the town centre, harbour and beach are only half a mile away, with direct access to the coastal footpath. A 4 acre site with 40 touring pitches, 20 hardstandings.

Leisure:

Facilities:

Services:

Within 3 miles:

Notes: Wi-fi

ST IVES

►►► 90% Little Trevarrack Holiday Park

Laity Ln, Carbis Bay TR26 3HW

☎ 01736 797580

e-mail: info@littletrevarrack.co.uk

dir: *A30 onto A3074 signed 'Carbis Bay & St Ives'. Left opposite turn to beach. 150yds, over x-rds, site 2nd on right*

* £12.50-£23 £12.50-£23

Open Apr-Sep (rs Etr-Whit, mid-end Sep games room & pool closed) Last arrival 21.30hrs Last departure 10.00hrs

A pleasant grass park set in countryside but close to beaches and local amenities. Plenty of tree planting will result in more shelter and privacy in this landscaped park, and there are superb sea views. A private bus service runs to St Ives in high season. A 20 acre site with 200 touring pitches.

Leisure:

Facilities:

Services:

Within 3 miles:

Notes: No groups. Sports area, recycling facilities, night warden. Wi-fi

ST IVES

►►► 80% Trevalgan Touring Park

Trevalgan TR26 3BJ

☎ 01736 792048

e-mail: recept@trevalgantouringpark.co.uk

dir: *From A30 follow holiday route to St Ives. B3311 through Halsetown to B3306. Left towards Land's End. Site signed 0.5m on right*

* £12.75-£21.25 £12.75-£21.25 £12.75-£21.25

Open Etr-Sep Last arrival 22.00hrs Last departure 10.00hrs

An open park next to a working farm in a rural area on the coastal road from St Ives to Zennor. The park is surrounded by mature hedges, but there are extensive views out over the sea. There are very good toilet facilities including family rooms, and a large TV lounge and recreation room with drinks machine. A 4.9 acre site with 120 touring pitches.

Leisure:

Facilities:

Services:

Within 3 miles:

Notes: Farm trail, crazy golf

ST IVES

►►► 79% Penderleath Caravan & Camping Park

Towednack TR26 3AF

☎ 01736 798403

e-mail: holidays@penderleath.co.uk

dir: *From A30 take A3074 towards St Ives. Left at 2nd mini-rdbt, approx 3m to T-junct. Left then immediately right. Next left*

* £12-£22.50 £12-£22.50 £12-£22.50

Open Etr-Oct Last arrival 21.30hrs Last departure 10.30hrs

Set in a rugged rural location, this tranquil park has extensive views towards St Ives Bay and the north coast. Facilities are all housed in modernised granite barns, and include a quiet licensed bar with beer garden, breakfast room and bar meals. The owners are welcoming and helpful. A 10 acre site with 75 touring pitches.

Leisure:

Facilities:

Services:

Within 3 miles:

Notes: Dogs must be well behaved & kept on a lead at all times. Bus to St Ives operates in high season

ST JUST (NEAR LAND'S END)

►►► 78% Kelynack Caravan & Camping Park

Kelynack TR19 7RE

☎ 01736 787633 01736 787633

e-mail: kelynackholidays@tiscali.co.uk

dir: *1m S of St Just, 5m N of Land's End on B3306*

£12-£14 £12-£14 £12-£14

Open Apr-Oct Last arrival 22.00hrs Last departure 10.00hrs

A small secluded park situated alongside a stream in an unspoilt rural location. The level grass pitches are in two areas, and the park is close to many coves, beaches and ancient villages. A 3 acre site with 20 touring pitches, 3 hardstandings and 13 statics.

Leisure:

Facilities:

Services:

Within 3 miles:

Notes: Dining & cooking shelter. Wi-fi

ST JUST (NEAR LAND'S END)

►►► 77% Roselands Caravan and Camping Park

Dowran TR19 7RS

☎ 01736 788571

e-mail: info@roselands.co.uk

dir: *From A30 Penzance bypass turn right for St Just on A3071. 5m, turn left after tin mine chimney at sign, follow signs to site*

Open all year Last arrival 21.00hrs Last departure 11.00hrs

A small, friendly park in a sheltered rural setting, an ideal location for a quiet family holiday. The owners continue to upgrade the park, and in addition to the attractive little bar there is an indoor games room, children's playground and good toilet facilities. A 3 acre site with 15 touring pitches and 15 statics.

Leisure:

Facilities:

Services:

Within 3 miles:

Notes: No cars by caravans. Wi-fi

ST JUST (NEAR LAND'S END)

►►► 76% Trevaylor Caravan & Camping Park

Botallack TR19 7PU

☎ 01736 787016

e-mail: trevaylor@cornishcamping.co.uk

dir: *On B3306 (St Just-St Ives road), site on right 0.75m from St Just*

* £4-£7 £4-£7 £4-£7

Open Fri before Etr-Oct Last departure noon

A sheltered grassy site located off the beaten track in a peaceful location at the western tip of Cornwall. The dramatic coastline and the pretty villages nearby are truly unspoilt. Clean, well-maintained facilities and a good shop are offered along with a bar serving meals. A 6 acre site with 50 touring pitches and 4 statics.

Leisure:

Facilities:

Services:

Within 3 miles:

ST JUST-IN-ROSELAND

►►►► 84% Trethem Mill Touring Park

TR2 5JF

☎ 01872 580504 01872 580968

e-mail: reception@trethem.com

dir: *From Tregony on A3078 to St Mawes. 2m after Trewithian, follow signs to site*

* £15-£22 £15-£22 £15-£22

Open Apr-mid Oct Last arrival 20.00hrs Last departure 11.00hrs

A quality park in all areas, with upgraded amenities including a reception, shop, laundry, and disabled/family room. This carefully-tended and sheltered park is in a lovely rural setting, with spacious pitches separated by young trees and shrubs. The very keen family who own it are continually looking for ways to enhance its facilities. An 11 acre site with 84 touring pitches, 50 hardstandings.

Leisure:
Facilities:
Services:
Within 3 miles:
Notes: Information centre. Wi-fi

ST MABYN

►►► 86% Glenmorris Park

Longstone Rd PL30 3BY

☎ 01208 841677 01208 841514

e-mail: info@glenmorris.co.uk

web: www.glenmorris.co.uk

dir: *S of Camelford on A39, left after BP garage onto B3266 to Bodmin, 6m to Longstone, right at x-rds to St Mabyn, site approx 400mtrs on right*

Open Apr-Oct (rs Etr-Spring BH swimming pool may be closed) Last arrival 23.00hrs Last departure noon

A family-run site close to the market town of Wadebridge, and close to Bodmin. The park is in a peaceful country setting and at the same time provides plenty of on-site activities. Holiday chalets and fully-equipped holiday homes are available to rent, along with a choice of pitches. Seasonal touring pitches available. A 12 acre site with 120 touring pitches, 47 hardstandings and 16 statics.

Leisure: **Facilities:** **Services:** **Within 3 miles:** **Notes:** Quiet from 23.00hrs-7.00hrs. Small animal area. Wi-fi

ST MERRYN (NEAR PADSTOW)

78% Harlyn Sands Holiday Park

Lighthouse Rd, Trevose Head PL28 8SQ

☎ 01841 520720 01841 521251

e-mail: harlyn@freenet.co.uk

web: www.harlynsands.co.uk

dir: *Exit B3276 in St Merryn centre onto unclassified road towards Harlyn Sands & Trevose Head. Follow brown site signs for approx 1m. (NB Do not turn right to Harlyn Sands)*

Open Etr-Nov Last arrival 22.00hrs Last departure 10.00hrs

A family park for 'bucket and spade' holidays, surrounded by seven bays each with its own sandy beach. On site entertainment for both children and adults is extensive, and there is an indoor swimming pool complex, excellent restaurant and takeaway, plus an over-30s lounge bar. A 21 acre site with 160 touring pitches, 6 hardstandings and 350 statics.

Leisure: **Facilities:** **Services:** **Within 3 miles:** **Notes:** Families only. Arcade, clubhouse, chip shop. Wi-fi

ST MERRYN (NEAR PADSTOW)

►►►► 80% Carnevas Holiday Park & Farm Cottages

Carnevas Farm PL28 8PN

☎ 01841 520230 & 521209

01841 520230

e-mail: carnevascampsite@aol.com

dir: *From St Merryn on B3276 towards Porthcothan Bay. Approx 2m turn right at site sign onto unclass road opposite Tredrea Inn. Site 0.25m on right*

* £9-£16 £9-£16 £9-£16

Open Apr-Oct (rs Apr-Whit & mid Sep-Oct shop, bar & restaurant closed)

A family-run park on a working farm, divided into four paddocks on slightly sloping grass. The toilets are central to all areas, and there is a small licensed bar serving bar meals. An 8 acre site with 195 touring pitches and 14 statics.

Leisure:

Facilities:

Services:

Within 3 miles:

Notes: No skateboards. 2 family bathrooms. Wi-fi

ST MERRYN (NEAR PADSTOW)

Atlantic Bays Holiday Park

St Merryn PL28 8PY

01841 520855 01841 520419

e-mail: info@pointcurlew.com

dir: *Take B3274 towards Padstow, in 3m left onto unclassified road to St Merryn, follow brown signs to park*

Open all year

A completely re-developed park for the 2010 season (formerly called the Point Curlew Chalet & Touring Park), with a mix of hardstanding and grass pitches. There will be a new, high quality toilet/shower block and a comfortable bar/restaurant. The park is set in a rural area yet only two miles from the coast and beautiful beaches. At the time of going to press the rating for this site had not been confirmed. For up-to-date information please see the AA website: theAA.com. 70 touring pitches and 165 statics.

Leisure:

Facilities:

Services:

Within 3 miles:

ST MINVER

►►►► 80% Gunvenna Caravan Park

PL27 6QN

01208 862405 01208 869107

dir: *From A39, N of Wadebridge take B3314 (Port Isaac road), site 4m on right*

Open Etr-Oct Last arrival 21.00hrs Last departure 11.00hrs

An attractive park with extensive rural views in a quiet country location, yet within three miles of Polzeath. This popular park is family owned and run, and provides good facilities in an ideal position for touring north Cornwall. New hardstanding pitches, improved landscaping and static caravans and a cottage for holiday hire. A 10 acre site with 75 touring pitches, 5 hardstandings and 44 statics.

Leisure:

Facilities:

Services:

Within 3 miles:

Notes: Wi-fi

SENNEN

►►► 74% Sennen Cove Camping & Caravanning Club Site

Higher Tregiffian Farm TR19 6JB

☎ 01736 871588

dir: *A30 towards Land's End. Right onto A3306 St Just/Pendeen Rd. Site 200yds on left*

Open 27 Apr-28 Sep Last arrival 21.00hrs Last departure noon

Set in a rural area with distant views of Carn Brae and the coast just two miles from Land's End, this very good club site is well run with modern, clean facilities. It offers a children's play field, late arrivals area and a dog-exercising paddock. A 4 acre site with 72 touring pitches, 6 hardstandings.

Leisure:

Facilities:

Services:

Within 3 miles:

Notes: Site gates closed 23.00hrs-07.00hrs

SUMMERCOURT

RV ►►►► 95% Carvynick Country Club

TR8 5AF

☎ 01872 510716 01872 510172

e-mail: info@carvynick.co.uk

web: www.carvynick.co.uk

dir: *Off A3058*

Open all year (rs Jan-early Feb restricted leisure facilities)

Set within the gardens of an attractive country estate this spacious dedicated American RV Park (also home to the 'Itchy Feet' retail company) provides all full-facility pitches on hardstandings. The extensive on-site amenities, shared by the high quality time share village, include an excellent restaurant with lounge bar, indoor leisure area with swimming pool, fitness suite and badminton court. 47 touring pitches.

Leisure:

Services:

Within 3 miles:

Notes: Dogs must be exercised off site

TINTAGEL

►►► 70% Headland Caravan & Camping Park

Atlantic Rd PL34 0DE

☎ 01840 770239 01840 770925

e-mail: headland.caravan@talktalkbusiness.net

dir: *From B3263 follow brown tourist signs through village to Headland*

Open Etr-Oct Last arrival 21.00hrs

A peaceful family-run site in the mystical village of Tintagel, close to the ruins of King Arthur's Castle. The Cornish coastal path and the spectacular scenery are just two of the attractions here, and there are safe bathing beaches nearby. Holiday static caravans for hire. A 5 acre site with 62 touring pitches and 28 statics.

Leisure:

Facilities:

Services:

Within 3 miles:

Notes: Dogs must be kept on short leads & exercised off site. Quiet after 23.00hrs

TORPOINT

►►►► 78% Whitsand Bay Lodge & Touring Park

Millbrook PL10 1JZ

☎ 01752 822597 01752 823444

e-mail: enquiries@whitsandbayholidays.co.uk

dir: *From Torpoint take A374, turn left at Anthony onto B3247 for 1.25m to T-junct. Turn left, 0.25m then right onto Cliff Rd. Site 2m on left*

£10-£25 £10-£25

Open Apr-Sep Last arrival 19.00hrs Last departure 10.00hrs

A very well equipped park with panoramic coastal, sea and countryside views from its terraced pitches. An ambitious programme of development has resulted in a very high quality park with upmarket toilet facilities and other amenities. A 27 acre site with 49 touring pitches, 30 hardstandings and 5 statics.

Leisure:

Facilities:

Services:

Within 3 miles:

Notes: Families & couples only. No tents. Bar open at weekends. Sauna, sunbed, entertainment, putting, chapel, library

TRURO

►►►►► 91% Carnon Downs Caravan & Camping Park

Carnon Downs TR3 6JJ

☎ 01872 862283 📠 01872 870820

e-mail: info@carnon-downs-caravanpark.co.uk

dir: *Take A39 from Truro towards Falmouth. Site just off main Carnon Downs rdbt, on left*

* £17.70-£25.50 £17.70-£25.50 £14.70-£22.50

Open all year Last arrival 22.00hrs Last departure 11.00hrs

A beautifully upgraded, mature park set in meadowland and woodland close to the village amenities of Carnon Downs. The four toilet blocks provide exceptional facilities in bright modern surroundings. An extensive landscaping programme has been carried out to give more spacious pitch sizes, and there is an exciting children's playground with modern equipment, and a football pitch. A 33 acre site with 150 touring pitches, 80 hardstandings and 1 static.

Leisure: **Facilities:** **Services:** **Within 3 miles:** **Notes:** Baby & child bathroom, 3 family bathrooms

TRURO

►►►► 80% Truro Caravan and Camping Park

TR4 8QN

☎ 01872 560274 📠 01872 561413

e-mail: info@liskey.co.uk

dir: *Exit A390 at Threemilestone rdbt onto unclass road towards Chacewater. Site signed on right in 0.5m*

Open all year Last arrival 21.00hrs Last departure 10.30hrs

An attractive south-facing park divided into paddocks by mature hedging, and with quality modern toilets. It is located on the fringes of an urban area a few miles from the city, and almost equidistant from both the rugged north coast and the calmer south coastal areas. There is a bus from the gate to the city of Truro. 15 seasonal touring pitches available. An 8.5 acre site with 51 touring pitches, 26 hardstandings and 49 statics.

Leisure:

Facilities:

Services:

Within 3 miles:

Notes: No bicycles or skateboards. Play area. Wi-fi

VERYAN

►►► 76% Veryan Camping & Caravanning Club Site

Tretheake Manor TR2 5PP

☎ 01872 501658

dir: *Exit A3078 at filling station signed Veryan/Portloe onto unclassified road. Site signed on left*

Open 2 Apr-2 Nov Last arrival 21.00hrs Last departure noon

A quiet park on slightly undulating land with pleasant countryside views. A tranquil fishing lake holds appeal for anglers, and the site is just 2.5 miles from one of Cornwall's finest sandy beaches. A 9 acre site with 150 touring pitches, 24 hardstandings.

Leisure:

Facilities:

Services:

Within 3 miles:

Notes: Site gates closed 23.00hrs-07.00hrs

WADEBRIDGE

►►► 74% Little Bodieve Holiday Park

Bodieve Rd PL27 6EG

☎ 01208 812323

e-mail: info@littlebodieve.co.uk

dir: *From A39 rdbt on Wadebridge by-pass take B3314 signed Rock/Port Isaac, site 0.25m on right*

Open Apr-Oct (rs Early & late season pool, shop & clubhouse closed) Last arrival 20.00hrs Last departure 11.00hrs

Rurally located with pitches in three large grassy paddocks, this family park is close to the Camel Estuary. The licensed clubhouse provides bar meals, with an entertainment programme in high season, and the swimming pool has a sun terrace plus a separate waterslide and splash pool. There are 7 static holiday caravans for hire. A 22 acre site with 195 touring pitches and 75 statics.

Leisure:

Facilities:

Services:

Within 3 miles:

Notes: Families & couples only. Crazy golf, water shute/splash pool, pets' corner

WATERGATE BAY

►►►► 79% Watergate Bay Touring Park

Watergate Bay TR8 4AD

☎ 01637 860387 ▤ 0871 661 7549

e-mail: email@watergatebaytouringpark.co.uk

web: www.watergatebaytouringpark.co.uk

dir: *4m N of Newquay on B3276 (coast road)*

* £10-£18 £10-£18 £10-£18

Open Mar-Oct (rs Mar-22 May & 13 Sep-Oct restricted bar, cafe, shop & pool) Last arrival 22.00hrs Last departure noon

A well-established park above Watergate Bay, where acres of golden sand, rock pools and surf are seen as a holidaymakers' paradise. Toilet facilities are appointed to a high standard, and there is a wide range of activities, including a regular entertainment programme in the clubhouse. A 30 acre site with 171 touring pitches, 14 hardstandings and 2 statics.

Leisure:

Facilities:

Services:

Within 3 miles:

Notes: Entertainment, free minibus to beach. Wi-fi

WIDEMOUTH BAY

71% Widemouth Bay Caravan Park

EX23 0DF

☎ 01271 866766 ▤ 01271 866791

e-mail: bookings@jfhols.co.uk

dir: *Take Widemouth Bay coastal road off A39, turn left. Site on left*

* £9-£32 £9-£32 £7-£32

Open Etr-Oct Last arrival dusk Last departure 10.00hrs

A partly sloping rural site set in countryside overlooking the sea and one of Cornwall's finest beaches. Nightly entertainment in high season with emphasis on children's and family club programmes. This park is located less than half a mile from the sandy beaches of Widemouth Bay. A 58 acre site with 220 touring pitches, 90 hardstandings and 200 statics.

Leisure:

Facilities:

Services:

Within 3 miles:

Notes: Wi-fi

WIDEMOUTH BAY

►►► 71% Penhalt Farm Holiday Park

EX23 0DG

☎ 01288 361210 🖷 01288 361210

e-mail: denandjennie@penhaltfarm.fsnet.co.uk

web: www.penhaltfarm.co.uk

dir: *From Bude take 2nd right to Widemouth Bay road off A39, left at end by Widemouth Manor signed Millook onto coastal road. Site 0.75m on left*

Open Etr-Oct

Splendid views of the sea and coast can be enjoyed from all pitches on this sloping but partly level site, set in a lovely rural area on a working farm. About one mile away is one of Cornwall's finest beaches, which is popular with all the family as well as surfers. An 8 acre site with 100 touring pitches.

Leisure:

Facilities:

Services:

Within 3 miles:

Notes: Pool table, netball & football posts, air hockey & table tennis

AMBLESIDE

►►►► 88% Skelwith Fold Caravan Park

LA22 0HX

☎ 015394 32277 🖷 015394 34344

e-mail: info@skelwith.com

dir: *From Ambleside on A593 towards Coniston, left at Clappersgate onto B5286 (Hawkshead road). Site 1m on right*

* £18.50-£23 £18.50-£23

Open Mar-15 Nov Last arrival dusk Last departure noon

In the grounds of a former mansion, this park is in a beautiful setting close to Lake Windermere. Touring areas are dotted in paddocks around the extensively wooded grounds, and the all-weather pitches are set close to the many facility buildings. There is a 5-acre family recreation area which has spectacular views of Loughrigg Fell. 40 seasonal touring pitches. A 130 acre site with 150 touring pitches, 150 hardstandings and 300 statics.

Leisure:

Facilities:

Services:

Within 3 miles:

Notes: Family recreation area. Wi-fi

APPLEBY-IN-WESTMORLAND

►►►►► 91% Wild Rose Park

Ormside CA16 6EJ

☎ 017683 51077 🖹 017683 52551

e-mail: reception@wildrose.co.uk

web: www.wildrose.co.uk

dir: *Signed on unclass road to Great Ormside, off B6260*

* £17-£25.50 £17-£25.50
£17-£25.50

Open all year (rs Nov-Mar shop & pool closed, restaurant rs) Last arrival 22.00hrs Last departure noon

Situated in the Eden Valley, this family-run park has been carefully landscaped and offers superb facilities, including four new wooden wigwams for hire. There are several individual pitches, and extensive views from most areas of the park. Traditional stone walls and lots of indigenous trees help it to blend into the environment. An 85 acre site with 226 touring pitches, 140 hardstandings and 273 statics.

Leisure: **Facilities:** **Services:** **Within 3 miles:**

Notes: No unaccompanied teenagers & no group bookings. No dangerous dogs. Tourist Information, pitch & putt

BARROW-IN-FURNESS

►►► 82% South End Caravan Park

Walney Island LA14 3YQ

☎ 01229 472823 & 471556

🖹 01229 472822

e-mail: enquiries@secp.co.uk

web: www.walneyislandcaravanpark.co.uk

dir: *M6 junct 36, A590 to Barrow, follow signs for Walney Island. Cross bridge, turn left. Site 6m south*

Open Mar-Oct (rs Mar-Etr & Oct pool closed) Last arrival 22.00hrs Last departure noon

A friendly family-owned and run park next to the sea and close to a nature reserve, on the southern end of Walney Island. It offers an extensive range of quality amenities including an adult lounge, and high standards of cleanliness and maintenance. A 7 acre site with 50 touring pitches, 20 hardstandings and 200 statics.

Leisure:

Facilities:

Services:

Within 3 miles:

Notes: Bowling green, snooker table

BOOT

►►►► 88% Eskdale Camping & Caravanning Club Site

Hollins Farm CA19 1TH

☎ 019467 23253

dir: *Exit A595 at Gosforth or Holmbrook to Eskdale Green & then to Boot. Site on left towards Hardknott Pass after railway*

Open Mar-Oct Last arrival 21.00hrs Last departure noon

A very pleasant site which has been extensively modernised and offers impressive facilities. The toilets and showers, laundries and CDP are matched by an extensive reception and well stocked shop. The electric hook-ups are cleverly tucked away. The park is only 0.25 miles from Boot station on the Ravenglass/Eskdale railway ('Ratty'). An 8 acre site with 80 touring pitches.

Leisure:

Facilities:

Services:

Within 3 miles:

Notes: Site gates closed 23.00hrs-07.00hrs

CROOKLANDS

►►► 82% Waters Edge Caravan Park

LA7 7NN

☎ 015395 67708

e-mail: ennis@watersedgecaravanpark.co.uk

dir: *M6 junct 36 take A65 towards Kirkby Lonsdale, at 2nd rdbt follow signs for Crooklands/Endmoor. Site 1m on right at Crooklands garage, just beyond 40mph limit*

* £14.20-£20.50 £14.20-£20.50 £11-£25

Open Mar-14 Nov (rs Low season bar not always open on week days) Last arrival 22.00hrs Last departure noon

A peaceful, well-run park close to the M6, bordered by streams and woodland. A Lakeland-style building houses a shop and bar, and the attractive toilet block is clean and modern. Ideal either as a stopover or for longer stays. 8 seasonal touring pitches available. A 3 acre site with 26 touring pitches, 18 hardstandings and 20 statics.

Leisure: **Facilities:** **Services:** **Within 3 miles:** **Notes:** Dogs must be kept on leads at all times

FLOOKBURGH

73% Lakeland Leisure Park

Moor Ln LA11 7LT

☎ 01539 558556 📠 01539 558559

dir: *On B5277 through Grange-over-Sands to Flookburgh. Left at village square, site 1m*

* £9-£70 £9-£70 £9-£52

Open mid Mar-Oct (rs Mar-May & Sep-Oct reduced activities, outdoor pool closed) Last arrival anytime Last departure 10.00hrs

A complete leisure park with full range of activities and entertainments, making this flat, grassy site ideal for families. The touring area is quietly situated away from the main amenities, but the swimming pools, all-weather bowling green and evening entertainment are just a short stroll away. 100 seasonal touring pitches. A 105 acre site with 190 touring pitches and 800 statics.

Leisure:

Facilities:

Services:

Within 3 miles:

Notes: No cars by caravans or tents. Family park. Wi-fi

GREAT LANGDALE

►►► 76% Great Langdale National Trust Campsite

LA22 9JU

☎ 015394 37668 📠 015394 37668

e-mail: langdale.camp@nationaltrust.org.uk

web: www.ntlakescampsites.org.uk

dir: *From Ambleside, A593 to Skelwith Bridge, right onto B5343, approx 5m to New Dungeon Ghyll Hotel. Site on left just before hotel*

Open all year Last arrival 22.00hrs Last departure 11.00hrs

Nestling in a green valley, sheltered by mature trees and surrounded by stunning fell views, this site is an ideal base for campers, climbers and walkers. The large grass tent area has some gravel parking for cars, and there is a separate area for groups, and one for families with a children's play area. Attractive wooden cabins house the toilets, a shop, and drying rooms, and there are wooden camping pods and two yurts for hire. A 9 acre site with 220 touring pitches.

Leisure: **Facilities:**

Services: **Within 3 miles:**

Notes: No groups of 4+, unless family with children. No noise between 23.00hrs-07.00hrs

KESWICK

►►►► 94% Castlerigg Hall Caravan & Camping Park

Castlerigg Hall CA12 4TE

☎ 017687 74499 017687 74499

e-mail: info@castlerigg.co.uk

dir: *1.5m SE of Keswick on A591, turn right at sign. Site 200mtrs on right past Heights Hotel*

£19-£23 £19-£23 £15-£19

Open mid Mar-7 Nov Last arrival 21.00hrs Last departure 11.30hrs

Spectacular views over Derwentwater to the mountains beyond are among the many attractions at this lovely Lakeland park. Old farm buildings have been converted into excellent toilets with private washing facilities and family bathroom, reception and a well-equipped shop, and there is a kitchen/dining area for campers, a restaurant/takeaway. There is a superb new toilet block and two wooden camping pods in the tent field. An 8 acre site with 48 touring pitches, 48 hardstandings and 30 statics.

Leisure: **Facilities:** **Services:** **Within 3 miles:** **Notes:** Dogs must be kept on leads & not unattended. Sitting room. Wi-fi

KIRKBY LONSDALE

►►►► 86% Woodclose Caravan Park

High Casterton LA6 2SE

☎ 01524 271597 01524 272301

e-mail: info@woodclosepark.com

web: www.woodclosepark.com

dir: *On A65, 0.25m after Kirkby Lonsdale towards Skipton, on left*

£12-£22 £12-£22 £13-£16

Open Mar-Oct Last arrival 21.00hrs Last departure noon

A peaceful park with excellent toilet facilities set in idyllic countryside in the Lune Valley. Ideal for those seeking quiet relaxation, and for visiting the Lakes and Dales, with the riverside walks at Devil's Bridge, and historic Kirkby Lonsdale both an easy walk away. There are three wigwam cabins for hire and Freeview TV is available via a booster cable from reception. A 9 acre site with 29 touring pitches, 8 hardstandings and 54 statics.

Leisure:

Facilities:

Services:

Within 3 miles:

Notes: No arrivals before 13.00hrs. Cycle hire, internet access. Wi-fi

PENRITH

►►►► 84% Lowther Holiday Park

Eamont Bridge CA10 2JB

☎ 01768 863631 ▤ 01768 868126

e-mail: sales@lowther-holidaypark.co.uk

dir: *3m S of Penrith on A6*

* £22.50-£30 £22.50-£30

£22.50-£30

Open mid Mar-mid Nov Last arrival 22.00hrs Last departure 22.00hrs

A secluded natural woodland site with lovely riverside walks and glorious surrounding countryside. The park is home to a rare colony of red squirrels, and trout fishing is available on the 2-mile stretch of the River Lowther which runs through it. A 50 acre site with 180 touring pitches, 50 hardstandings and 403 statics.

Leisure:

Facilities:

Services:

Within 3 miles:

Notes: Families only. No cats, rollerblades, skateboards or commercial vehicles

POOLEY BRIDGE

83% Park Foot Caravan & Camping Park

Howtown Rd CA10 2NA

☎ 017684 86309 ▤ 017684 86041

e-mail: holidays@parkfootullswater.co.uk

web: www.parkfootullswater.co.uk

dir: *M6 junct 40, A66 towards Keswick, then A592 to Ullswater. left for Pooley Bridge, right at church, right at x-roads signed Howtown*

* £17-£32 £15.50-£28

£12.50-£25

Open Mar-Oct (rs Mar-Apr, mid Sep-Oct clubhouse open wknds only) Last arrival 22.00hrs Last departure noon

A lively park with good outdoor sports facilities, and boat launching directly onto the lake. The park has many mature trees and views across the lake. The Country Club bar and restaurant provides meals, as well as discos, live music and entertainment. Lodges and static caravans for hire. An 18 acre site with 323 touring pitches and 131 statics.

Leisure: **Facilities:** **Services:** **Within 3 miles:**

Notes: Families & couples only. Pony trekking, pool table, table tennis, bike hire

POOLEY BRIDGE

►►► 80% Waterfoot Caravan Park

CA11 0JF

☎ 017684 86302 📠 017684 86728

e-mail: enquiries@waterfootpark.co.uk

web: www.waterfootpark.co.uk

dir: *M6 junct 40, A66 for 1m, then A592 for 4m, site on right before lake. (NB do not leave A592 until site entrance; Sat Nav not compatible)*

£18-£26 £18-£26

Open Mar-14 Nov Last arrival dusk Last departure noon

A quality touring park with hardstanding pitches in a grassy glade within the wooded grounds of an elegant Georgian mansion. Toilets facilities are clean and well maintained, and the lounge bar with a separate family room enjoys lake views. There is a path to Ullswater. Aira Force waterfall, Dalemain House and Pooley Bridge are all close by. Please note that there is no access via Dacre. A 22 acre site with 34 touring pitches, 30 hardstandings and 146 statics.

Leisure: **Facilities:** **Services:** **Within 3 miles:** **Notes:** Families only. No tents & no large RVS

SILLOTH

90% Stanwix Park Holiday Centre

Greenrow CA7 4HH

☎ 016973 32666 📠 016973 32555

e-mail: enquiries@stanwix.com

dir: *1m SW on B5300. From A596 (Wigton bypass), signs to Silloth on B5302. In Silloth signs to site, approx 1m on B5300*

* £19.30-£23.60 £19.30-£23.60 £19.30-£23.60

Open all year (rs Nov-Feb (ex New Year) no entertainment/shop closed) Last arrival 22.00hrs Last departure 11.00hrs

A large well-run family park within easy reach of the Lake District. Attractively laid out, with lots of amenities, including a 4-lane automatic, 10-pin bowling alley. Excellent touring areas with hardstandings, one in a peaceful glade well away from the main leisure complex. Campers' kitchen and clean, well-maintained toilet facilities. A 4 acre site with 121 touring pitches, 100 hardstandings and 212 statics.

Leisure: **Facilities:** **Services:** **Within 3 miles:** **Notes:** Amusement arcade & gym

SILLOTH

►► 66% Tanglewood Caravan Park

Causewayhead CA7 4PE

☎ 016973 31253

e-mail: tanglewoodcaravanpark@hotmail.com

dir: *Adjacent to B5302 (Wigton-Silloth), 4m from Abbeytown, site on left*

* £18 £18 £18

Open Mar-Jan Last arrival 23.00hrs Last departure 10.00hrs

A pleasant park sheltered by mature trees and shrubs, set in meadowland close to the town. There is a clubhouse and bar, and two small toilet blocks for tourers. A 7 acre site with 31 touring pitches, 21 hardstandings and 58 statics.

Leisure:

Facilities:

Services:

Within 3 miles:

ULVERSTON

►►►► 84% Bardsea Leisure Park

Priory Rd LA12 9QE

☎ 01229 584712 01229 580413

e-mail: reception@bardsealeisure.co.uk

dir: *Off A5087*

Open all year Last arrival 21.00hrs Last departure 18.00hrs

Attractively landscaped former quarry, making a quiet and very sheltered site. Many of the generously-sized pitches offer all-weather full facilities, and a luxury toilet block provides plenty of fully-serviced cubicles. Set on the southern edge of the town, convenient for both the coast and the Lake District. A 5 acre site with 83 touring pitches, 83 hardstandings and 83 statics.

Leisure:

Facilities:

Services:

Within 3 miles:

WATERMILLOCK

►►►► 84% The Quiet Site

Ullswater CA11 0LS

☎ 07768 727016

e-mail: info@thequietsite.co.uk

dir: *M6 junct 40, A592 towards Ullswater. Right at lake junct, then right at Brackenrigg Hotel. Site 1.5m on right*

* £17-£28 £17-£28 £12-£28

Open all year (rs Low season park open wknds only) Last arrival 22.00hrs Last departure noon

A well-maintained site in a lovely, peaceful location, with good terraced pitches offering great fells views, very good facilities including family bathrooms, and a charming olde-worlde bar. There are four camping pods and a newly-refurbished self-catering stone cottage for hire. A 10 acre site with 100 touring pitches, 60 hardstandings and 23 statics.

Leisure:

Facilities:

Services:

Within 3 miles:

Notes: Quiet from 22.00hrs onwards. Pets corner, pool/darts (for adults), caravan storage. Wi-fi

WATERMILLOCK

►►► 82% Ullswater Caravan, Camping & Marine Park

High Longthwaite CA11 0LR

☎ 017684 86666 017684 86095

e-mail: info@uccmp.co.uk

web: www.uccmp.co.uk

dir: *M6 junct 40 take A592, W for Ullswater for 5m. Right alongside Ullswater for 2m, then right at phone box. Site 0.5m on right*

* £19-£22 £19-£22 £16.50-£18.50

Open Mar-Nov (rs Low season bar open wknds only) Last arrival 21.00hrs Last departure noon

A pleasant rural site with own nearby boat launching and marine storage facility. The family-owned and run park enjoys fell and lake views, and there is a bar, café and fish and chip shop on site. Many of the pitches are fully serviced and there are two wooden cabins with barbecues. A 12 acre site with 160 touring pitches, 58 hardstandings and 55 statics.

Leisure: **Facilities:** **Services:** **Within 3 miles:** **Notes:** No open fires. Boat launching & moorings 1m

WINDERMERE

►►►► 85% Fallbarrow Park

Rayrigg Rd LA23 3DL

☎ 015394 44422 015394 88736

e-mail: enquiries@southlakelandparks.co.uk

dir: *0.5m N of Windermere on A591. At mini-rdbt take road to Bowness Bay & the Lake. Site 1.3m on right*

* £18.50-£30 £18.50-£30

Open Mar-mid Nov Last arrival 22.00hrs Last departure 10.00hrs

A park set in impressive surroundings just a few minutes walk from Bowness on the shore of Lake Windermere. There is direct access to the lake through the park. Good hedged fully-serviced pitches, quality toilet facilities, a deli and café serving meals and locally sourced produce, and 30 holiday hire statics. A 32 acre site with 38 touring pitches and 269 statics.

Leisure:

Facilities:

Services:

Within 3 miles:

Notes: No tents. Boat launching. Wi-fi

WINDERMERE

►►►► 85% Park Cliffe Camping & Caravan Estate

Birks Rd, Tower Wood LA23 3PG

☎ 01539 531344 01539 531971

e-mail: info@parkcliffe.co.uk

dir: *M6 junct 36, A590. Right at Newby Bridge onto A592. 3.6m right into site. (NB this is only advised direction for approaching site)*

* £23.50-£26.50 £23.50-£26.50 £18.75-£21.50

Open Mar-14 Nov (rs Wknds/school hols facilities open fully) Last arrival 22.00hrs Last departure noon

A lovely hillside park set in 25 secluded acres of fell land. The camping area is sloping and uneven in places, but well drained and sheltered; some pitches have great views of Lake Windermere and the Langdales. The park is very well equipped for families, and there is an attractive bar lounge. 3 static caravans for hire. A 25 acre site with 60 touring pitches, 60 hardstandings and 55 statics.

Leisure: **Facilities:** **Services:** **Within 3 miles:**

Notes: No noise 22.30hrs-07.30hrs. Off-licence, playground. Wi-fi

WINDERMERE

►►►► 82% Limefitt Park

Patterdale Rd, Troutbeck LA23 1PA

☎ 015394 32300 015394 32848

e-mail: enquiries@southlakelandparks.co.uk

dir: *From Windermere take A592 to Ullswater. Site 2.5m on right*

Open Mar-14 Nov Last arrival 22.00hrs Last departure 10.00hrs

An attractive family site with superb facilities in a lovely location in the Lake District National Park. Buildings are well integrated into the landscape, and the River Troutbeck runs through the grounds. From its valley setting there are spectacular views of the surrounding hills, with direct access to the fells and plenty of walks. A 20 acre site with 35 touring pitches, 35 hardstandings and 125 statics.

Leisure:

Facilities:

Services:

Within 3 miles:

Notes: No pets, skateboards, roller skates/ blades or electric scooters. Wi-fi

BAKEWELL

►►► 78% Greenhills Holiday Park

Crowhill Ln DE45 1PX

☎ 01629 813052 & 813467

01629 815760

e-mail: info@greenhillsholidaypark.co.uk

web: www.greenhillsholidaypark.co.uk

dir: *1m NW of Bakewell on A6. Signed before Ashford-in-the-Water, 50yds along unclass road on right*

* £10-£22 £10-£22 £8-£18

Open Feb-Nov (rs Mar, Apr & Oct bar & shop closed) Last arrival 22.00hrs Last departure noon

A well-established park set in lovely countryside within the Peak District National Park. Many pitches enjoy uninterrupted views, and there is easy accessibility to all facilities. A clubhouse, shop and children's playground are popular features. 40 seasonal touring pitches available. An 8 acre site with 172 touring pitches, 21 hardstandings and 63 statics.

Leisure:

Facilities:

Services:

Within 3 miles:

Notes: Wi-fi

BUXTON

►►►► 79% Lime Tree Park

Dukes Dr SK17 9RP

☎ 01298 22988 📠 01298 22988

e-mail: info@limetreeparkbuxton.co.uk

dir: *1m S of Buxton, between A515 & A6*

* fr £20 fr £20 fr £15

Open Mar-Oct Last arrival 21.00hrs Last departure noon

A most attractive and well-designed site, set on the side of a narrow valley in an elevated location. Its backdrop of magnificent old railway viaduct and views over Buxton and the surrounding hills make this a sought-after destination. 37 seasonal touring pitches available. A 10.5 acre site with 106 touring pitches, 22 hardstandings and 43 statics.

Leisure:

Facilities:

Services:

Within 3 miles:

NEWHAVEN

►►► 77% Newhaven Caravan & Camping Park

SK17 0DT

☎ 01298 84300 📠 01332 726027

e-mail: bobmacara@ntlworld.com

web: www.newhavencaravanpark.co.uk

dir: *Between Ashbourne & Buxton at A515 & A5012 junct*

* £11.25-£15.50 £11.25-£15.50 £11.25-£15.50

Open Mar-Oct Last arrival 23.00hrs Last departure any time

Pleasantly situated within the Peak District National Park, with mature trees screening the three touring areas. Very good toilet facilities cater for touring vans and a large tent field, and there's a restaurant adjacent to the site. A 30 acre site with 125 touring pitches, 18 hardstandings and 73 statics.

Leisure:

Facilities:

Services:

Within 3 miles:

RIPLEY

►►►► 77% Golden Valley Caravan & Camping Park

Coach Rd DE55 4ES ☎ 01773 513881

e-mail: enquiries@goldenvalleycaravanpark.co.uk

web: www.goldenvalleycaravanpark.co.uk

dir: *M1 junct 26, A610 to Codnor. Right at lights, then right onto Alfreton Rd. In 1m left onto Coach Rd, park on left. (NB ignore Sat Nav for last few miles, follow guide directions)*

Open all year Last arrival 21.00hrs Last departure noon

This park is set within 30 acres of woodland in the Amber Valley. The fully-serviced pitches are set out in informal groups in clearings amongst the trees. The park has a cosy bar and bistro with outside patio, a fully stocked fishing lake, an on-site jacuzzi and fully equipped fitness suite. There is also a wildlife pond. A 30 acre site with 45 touring pitches, 45 hardstandings and 1 statics.

Leisure: **Facilities:** **Services:** **Within 3 miles:**

Notes: No cars by caravans. No open fires or disposable BBQs. No noise after 22.30hrs.

ROWSLEY

►►► 73% Grouse & Claret

Station Rd DE4 2EB

☎ 01629 733233 01629 735194

e-mail: grouseandclaret.matlock@marstons.co.uk

dir: *M1 junct 29. Site on A6, 5m from Matlock & 3m from Bakewell*

Open all year Last arrival 20.00hrs Last departure noon

A well-designed, purpose-built park at the rear of an eating house on the A6 between Bakewell and Chatsworth, and adjacent to the New Peak Shopping Village. The park comprises a level grassy area running down to the river, and all pitches have hardstandings and electric hook-ups. A 2.5 acre site with 26 touring pitches, 26 hardstandings.

Leisure:

Facilities:

Services:

Within 3 miles:

Notes: No cars by tents. Dogs must be under strict control. Wi-fi

YOULGREAVE

► 72% Bakewell Camping & Caravanning Club Site

Hopping Farm DE45 1NA

☎ 01629 636555

dir: *A6/B5056, after 0.5m turn right to Youlgreave. Turn sharp left after church down Bradford Rd, opposite George Hotel. 0.5m to sign turn right*

Open 2 Apr-2 Nov Last arrival 21.00hrs Last departure noon

Ideal for touring and walking in the Peak District National Park, this gently sloping grass site is accessed through narrow streets and along unadopted hardcore. Own sanitary facilities essential. A 14 acre site with 100 touring pitches, 6 hardstandings.

Leisure:

Facilities:

Services:

Within 3 miles:

Notes: Site gates closed 23.00hrs-07.00hrs

ASHBURTON

►►►► 82% Parkers Farm Holiday Park

Higher Mead Farm TQ13 7LJ

☎ 01364 654869 01364 654004

e-mail: parkersfarm@btconnect.com

dir: *From Exeter on A38, take 2nd left after Plymouth 26m sign, at Alston, signed Woodland-Denbury. From Plymouth on A38 take A383 Newton Abbot exit, turn right across bridge, rejoin A38, then as above*

£9-£24 £9-£24 £7-£19

Open Etr-end Oct (rs Wknds only bar/restaurant open out of season) Last arrival 22.00hrs Last departure 10.00hrs

A well-developed site terraced into rising ground. Part of a working farm, this park offers well maintained, quality facilities. Large family rooms with two shower cubicles, large sink and toilet are ideal for families with small children. There are regular farm walks when all the family can meet the various animals. A 25 acre site with 100 touring pitches, 20 hardstandings and 18 statics.

Leisure: **Facilities:** **Services:** **Within 3 miles:** **Notes:** Large field for dog walking

ASHBURTON

►►►► 80% River Dart Country Park

Holne Park TQ13 7NP

☎ 01364 652511 📠 01364 652020

e-mail: info@riverdart.co.uk

web: www.riverdart.co.uk

dir: *M5 junct 31, A38 towards Plymouth. At Ashburton at Peartree junct follow brown site signs. Site 1m on left. (NB Peartree junct is 2nd exit at Ashburton - do not exit at Linhay junct narrow roads unsuitable for caravans)*

Open Apr-Sep (rs Low season café bar restricted opening hours) Last arrival 21.00hrs Last departure 11.00hrs

Set in 90 acres of parkland that was once part of a Victorian estate, with many specimen and exotic trees and colourful flowers. Outdoor activities for all ages including abseiling, caving and canoeing, plus high quality facilities. Dartmoor is not far. A 90 acre site with 170 touring pitches, 23 hardstandings.

Leisure: **Facilities:** **Services:** **Within 3 miles:** **Notes:** Adventure playground, climbing, canoeing. Wi-fi

AXMINSTER

►►►► 82% Andrewshayes Caravan Park

Dalwood EX13 7DY

☎ 01404 831225 📠 01404 831893

e-mail: info@andrewshayes.co.uk

web: www.andrewshayes.co.uk

dir: *On A35, 3m from Axminster. Turn N at Taunton Cross signed Stockland/Dalwood. Site 150mtrs on right*

* £11-£24 £11-£24 £11-£24

Open Mar-Nov (rs Sep-Nov shop, bar hrs ltd, pool shut Sep-mid May) Last arrival 22.00hrs Last departure 11.00hrs

An attractive family park within easy reach of Lyme Regis, Seaton, Branscombe and Sidmouth in an ideal touring location. This popular park offers modern toilet facilities, an outdoor swimming pool and a quiet, cosy bar with a wide-screen TV room. 100 seasonal touring pitches available. A 12 acre site with 150 touring pitches, 105 hardstandings and 80 statics.

Leisure:

Facilities:

Services:

Within 3 miles:

Notes: Dogs must be kept on leads

►►► 82% Hawkchurch Country Park

Hawkchurch EX13 5UL

☎ 01297 678402

e-mail: enquiries@hawkchurchpark.co.uk

dir: *From Axminster towards Charmouth on A35 left onto B3165. Left onto Wareham Rd, site on left, follow signs. (NB the lanes near Hawkchurch are narrow)*

Open 15 Feb-4 Jan Last arrival 18.00hrs Last departure 10.00hrs

This peaceful park is set in mature woodlands right on the Devon and Dorset border, with easy access to the Jurassic Coast Heritage Site, Lyme Regis, Charmouth and West Bay. The site has huge potential, with hardstandings plus tent and rally fields, and the new owners plan to upgrade and improve the facilities. 125 seasonal touring pitches available. A 12 acre site with 369 touring pitches, 225 hardstandings.

Leisure:

Facilities:

Services:

Within 3 miles:

Notes: Wi-fi

BERRYNARBOR

►►► 84% Mill Park

Mill Ln EX34 9SH

☎ 01271 882647

e-mail: millparkdevon@btconnect.com

dir: *M5 junct 27 onto A361 towards Barnstaple. Right onto A399 towards Combe Martin. At Sawmills Inn take turn opposite for Berrynarbor*

Open Mar-30 Oct (rs High season on site facilities open) Last arrival 22.00hrs Last departure 10.00hrs

This family owned and run park is set in an attractive wooded valley with a stream running into a lake where coarse fishing is available. There is a quiet bar/restaurant with a family room. The park is two miles from Combe Martin and Ilfracombe and just a stroll across the road from the small harbour at Watermouth. Seasonal touring pitches available. A 23 acre site with 178 touring pitches, 20 hardstandings and 1 static.

Leisure:

Facilities:

Services:

Within 3 miles:

Notes: No large groups

BICKINGTON (NEAR ASHBURTON)

►►►► 80% Lemonford Caravan Park

TQ12 6JR

☎ 01626 821242 & 821263

01626 821263

e-mail: mark@lemonford.co.uk

web: www.lemonford.co.uk

dir: *From Exeter on A38 take A382, then 3rd exit at rdbt, follow Bickington signs*

* £10-£18 £10-£18 £10-£18

Open all year Last arrival 22.00hrs Last departure 11.00hrs

Small, secluded and well-maintained park with a good mixture of attractively laid out pitches. The friendly owners pay a great deal of attention to detail, and the toilets in particular are kept spotlessly clean. This good touring base is only one mile from Dartmoor and ten miles from the seaside at Torbay. A 7 acre site with 82 touring pitches, 55 hardstandings and 44 statics.

Leisure:

Facilities:

Services:

Within 3 miles:

Notes: Clothes drying area

BRAUNTON

►►►► 85% Hidden Valley Park

EX34 8NU

☎ 01271 813837

e-mail: relax@hiddenvalleypark.com

dir: *Direct access off A361, 8m from Barnstaple & 2m from Mullacott Cross*

* £15-£40 £15-£40 £15-£40

Open all year (rs 15 Nov-15 Mar all weather pitches only) Last arrival 21.00hrs Last departure 10.00hrs

A delightful, well-appointed family site set in a wooded valley, with superb facilities and a café. The park is set in a very rural, natural position not far from the beautiful coastline around Ilfracombe. A 25 acre site with 115 touring pitches, 65 hardstandings.

Leisure:

Facilities:

Services:

Within 3 miles:

Notes: Gardens, woodland walks & lake. Wi-fi

BRIDESTOWE

►►► 75% Bridestowe Caravan Park

EX20 4ER

☎ 01837 861261

e-mail: ali.young53@btinternet.com

dir: *Exit A30 at A386/Sourton Cross junct, follow B3278 signed Bridestowe, turn left in 3m. In village centre, left down unclass road for 0.5m*

Open Mar-Dec Last arrival 22.30hrs Last departure noon

A small, well-established park in a rural setting close to Dartmoor National Park. This mainly static park has a small, peaceful touring space, and there are many activities to enjoy in the area including fishing and riding. Part of the National Cycle Route 27 - the Devon coast to coast - passes close to this park. A 1 acre site with 13 touring pitches, 3 hardstandings and 40 statics.

Leisure:

Facilities:

Services:

Within 3 miles:

Notes:

BRIDGERULE

►►► 82% Hedleywood Caravan & Camping Park

EX22 7ED

☎ 01288 381404 01288 382011

e-mail: alan@hedleywood.co.uk

dir: *From B3254 take Widemouth road (unclass) at the Devon/Cornwall border*

* £10-£16 £10-£16 £10-£16

Open all year (rs Main hols bar/restaurant open) Last arrival anytime Last departure anytime

Set in a very rural location about four miles from Bude, this relaxed family-owned site has a peaceful, easy-going atmosphere. Pitches are in separate paddocks, some with extensive views, and this wooded park is quite sheltered in the lower areas. A 16.5 acre site with 120 touring pitches, 14 hardstandings and 16 statics.

Leisure:

Facilities:

Services:

Within 3 miles:

Notes: Dog kennels. Nature trail & dog walk. Wi-fi

BRIXHAM

►►► 78% Galmpton Touring Park

Greenway Rd TQ5 0EP

☎ 01803 842066

e-mail: galmptontouringpark@hotmail.com

dir: *Signed from A3022 (Torbay to Brixham road) at Churston*

* £11.70-£18.10 £11.70-£18.10 £11.70-£18.10

Open Etr-Sep Last arrival 21.00hrs Last departure 11.00hrs

An excellent location on high ground overlooking the River Dart, with outstanding views of the creek and anchorage. Pitches are set on level terraces, and facilities are bright and clean. A 10 acre site with 120 touring pitches, 15 hardstandings.

Leisure:

Facilities:

Services:

Within 3 miles:

Notes: Families & couples only. Dogs not accepted during peak season. Bathroom for under 5s (charged)

COMBE MARTIN

►►►► 87% Stowford Farm Meadows

Berry Down EX34 0PW

☎ 01271 882476 01271 883053

e-mail: enquiries@stowford.co.uk

dir: *M5 junct 27 onto A361 to Barnstaple. Take A39 from town centre towards Lynton, in 1m turn left onto B3230. Right at garage at Lynton Cross onto A3123, site 1.5m on right*

Open all year (rs Winter pool & bars closed) Last arrival 20.00hrs Last departure 10.00hrs

Very gently sloping, grassy, sheltered and south-facing site approached down a wide, well-kept driveway. This large farm park is set in 500 acres, and offers many quality amenities, including a large swimming pool, horse riding and crazy golf. A 60-acre wooded nature trail is an added attraction, as is the mini zoo with its stock of friendly animals. A 100 acre site with 700 touring pitches, 70 hardstandings.

Leisure:

Facilities:

Services:

Within 3 miles:

Notes: Cycle hire, caravan accessory shop

COMBE MARTIN

►►► 78% Newberry Valley Park

Woodlands EX34 0AT

☎ 01271 882334

e-mail: relax@newberryvalleypark.co.uk

dir: *M5 junct 27, A361 to North Aller rdbt. Right onto A399, through Combe Martin to sea. Left into site*

* £9-£35 £9-£35 £9-£35

Open Mar-Sep Last arrival 20.45hrs Last departure 10.00hrs

A family owned and run touring park on the edge of Combe Martin, with all its amenities just five minutes walk away. The park is set in a wooded valley with its own coarse fishing lake. The safe beaches of Newberry and Combe Martin are reached by a short footpath opposite the park entrance, where the South West coast path is located. A 20 acre site with 125 touring pitches.

Leisure:

Facilities:

Services:

Within 3 miles:

Notes: No camp fires

CROCKERNWELL

►►►► 76% Dartmoor Barley Meadow Camping & Caravanning Club Site

EX6 6NR

☎ 01647 281629

e-mail: welcome@barleymeadow.com

dir: *M5 junct 31, A30 to 3rd exit signed Woodleigh. Through Cheriton Bishop, site signed just beyond Crockernwell. From Cornwall take A30, at Whiddon Down junct take exit to Cheriton Bishop, site 3m on right*

* £14.20-£25.93 £14.20-£25.93 £11.64-£25.93

Open 12 Mar-2 Nov Last arrival 22.00hrs Last departure noon

A small, very well maintained park set on high ground in the Dartmoor National Park in a quiet location. The grassy pitches are mostly level, and the park is well placed to explore Dartmoor. A 4 acre site with 60 touring pitches, 20 hardstandings.

Leisure: **Facilities:** **Services:**

Within 3 miles:

Notes: Croissants/baguettes baked daily. Wi-fi

CROYDE

►►► 78% Bay View Farm Caravan & Camping Park

EX33 1PN

☎ 01271 890501

dir: *M5 junct 27 onto A361, through Barnstaple to Braunton, turn left onto B3231. Site at entry to Croyde village*

Open Mar-Oct Last arrival 21.30hrs Last departure 11.00hrs

A very busy and popular park close to surfing beaches and rock pools, with a public footpath leading directly to the sea. Set in a stunning location with views out over the Atlantic to Lundy Island, it is just a short stroll from Croyde. Facilities are clean and well maintained, and there is a fish and chip shop on site. No dogs allowed. A 10 acre site with 70 touring pitches, 38 hardstandings and 3 statics.

Leisure:

Facilities:

Services:

Within 3 miles:

Notes:

CROYDE BAY

84% Ruda Holiday Park

EX33 1NY

☎ 0844 335 3756 01271 890656

e-mail: touringandcamping@parkdeanholidays.com

web: www.parkdeantouring.com

dir: *M5 junct 27, A361 to Braunton. Left at main lights, follow Croyde signs*

* £13-£44 £13-£44 £13-£44

Open mid Mar-Nov Last arrival 21.00hrs Last departure 10.00hrs

A spacious, well-managed park, with its own glorious award winning sandy beach, is a surfers' paradise. Set in well-landscaped grounds, and with a full leisure programme plus daytime and evening entertainment for all the family. Cascades tropical adventure pool and an entertainment lounge are very popular features. A 220 acre site with 306 touring pitches and 289 statics.

Leisure:

Facilities:

Services:

Within 3 miles:

Notes: No pets. Family entertainment, children's clubs. Coast Bar & Kitchen. Wi-fi

DARTMOUTH

►►►► 92%
Woodlands Leisure Park

Blackawton TQ9 7DQ

☎ 01803 712598 🖹 01803 712680

e-mail: fun@woodlandspark.com

web: www.woodlands-caravanpark.com

dir: *4m from Dartmouth on A3122. From A38 take turn for Totnes & follow brown tourist signs*

* £13.50-£21 £13.50-£21 £13.50-£21

Open Etr-7 Nov Last departure 11.00hrs

A quality caravan or tent park with excellent facilities, spacious pitches and good attention to detail, all set in an extensive woodland environment with a terraced grass camping area. Free entry to the adjoining Woodlands Family Theme Park makes an excellent package holiday for families but also good for just adults seeking a low season break. A 16 acre site with 350 touring pitches, 50 hardstandings.

Leisure: Facilities: Services: Within 3 miles:

Notes: Watercoasters, toboggan run, gliders, falconry centre

DAWLISH

80%
Lady's Mile Holiday Park

EX7 0LX

☎ 01626 863411 🖹 01626 888689

e-mail: info@ladysmile.co.uk

dir: *1m N of Dawlish on A379*

* £11.50-£25 £11.50-£25 £11.50-£25

Open 17 Mar-27 Oct Last arrival 20.00hrs Last departure 11.00hrs

A holiday site with all grass touring pitches, and plenty of activities for everyone. Two swimming pools with waterslides, a large adventure playground, 9-hole golf course, and a bar with entertainment in high season all add to the enjoyment of a stay here. Facilities are kept clean, and the surrounding beaches are easily accessed. A 16 acre site with 243 touring pitches and 43 statics.

Leisure:

Facilities:

Services:

Within 3 miles:

Notes: Wi-fi

DAWLISH

78% Peppermint Park

Warren Rd EX7 0PQ

☎ 01626 863436 01626 866482

e-mail: info@peppermintpark.co.uk

web: www.peppermintpark.co.uk

dir: *From A379 at Dawlish follow signs for Dawlish Warren. Site 1m on left at bottom of hill*

Open Etr-end Oct Last arrival 21.00hrs Last departure 10.00hrs

A well managed, attractive park close to the coast, with excellent facilities including a club and bar which are well away from pitches. Nestling close to sandy beaches, the park offers individually marked pitches on level terraces in pleasant, sheltered grassland. The many amenities include a heated swimming pool and water chute, coarse fishing and a launderette. A 26 acre site with 250 touring pitches, 15 hardstandings and 57 statics.

Leisure:

Facilities:

Services:

Within 3 miles:

Notes: Families & couples only. Wi-fi

DAWLISH

74% Golden Sands Holiday Park

Week Ln EX7 0LZ

☎ 01626 863099 01626 867149

e-mail: info@goldensands.co.uk

dir: *M5 junct 30 onto A379 signed Dawlish. After 6m pass small harbour at Cockwood, signed on left in 2m*

Open 21 Mar-Oct Last arrival noon Last departure 10.00hrs

A holiday centre for all the family, offering a wide range of entertainment. The small touring area is surrounded by mature trees and hedges in a pleasant area, and visitors enjoy free use of the licensed club, and heated swimming pools. Organised children's activities are a popular feature, and the facilities of neighbouring Peppermint Park are open to all visitors. A 12 acre site with 23 touring pitches.

Leisure:

Facilities:

Services:

Within 3 miles:

DAWLISH

►►►► 82% Cofton Country Holidays

Starcross EX6 8RP

☎ 01626 890111 🖷 01626 891572

e-mail: info@coftonholidays.co.uk

dir: *On A379 (Exeter/Dawlish road) 3m from Dawlish*

* £13-£26 £13-£26 £13-£26

Open all year (rs Etr-Spring BH & mid Sep-Oct swimming pool closed) Last arrival 20.00hrs Last departure 11.00hrs

Set in a rural location surrounded by spacious open grassland, with plenty of well-kept flower beds throughout the park. Most pitches overlook either the swimming pool complex or the fishing lakes and woodlands. An on-site pub serves drinks, and meals or snacks, for all the family, and a mini-market caters for most shopping needs. 110 seasonal touring pitches available. A 45 acre site with 450 touring pitches, 30 hardstandings and 76 statics.

Leisure:

Facilities:

Services:

Within 3 miles:

Notes: Families only. Coarse fishing, pub with family room. Wi-fi

EAST WORLINGTON

►►►► 75% Yeatheridge Farm Caravan Park

EX17 4TN

☎ 01884 860330

e-mail: yeatheridge@talk21.com

dir: *M5 junct 27, A361, at 1st rdbt at Tiverton take B3137 for 9m towards Witheridge. Fork left 1m past Nomansland onto B3042. Site on left in 3.5m. (NB Do not go to East Worlington)*

Open Etr-Sep Last arrival 22.00hrs Last departure 22.00hrs

A gently sloping grass site with mature trees, set in meadowland in rural Devon. There are good views of distant Dartmoor, and the site is of great appeal to families with its farm animals, horse riding, and two indoor swimming pools, one with flume. There are many attractive villages in this area. A 9 acre site with 85 touring pitches and 12 statics.

Leisure:

Facilities:

Services:

Within 3 miles:

Notes: Fishing, pool table. Wi-fi

EXMOUTH

90% Devon Cliffs Holiday Park

Sandy Bay EX8 5BT

☎ 01395 226226 01395 226267

e-mail: bob.sleighton@bourne-leisure.co.uk

dir: *M5 junct 30/A376 towards Exmouth, follow brown signs to Sandy Bay*

* £17-£114 £17-£114

Open mid Mar-Oct (rs mid Mar-May & Sep-Oct some facilities may be reduced) Last arrival anytime Last departure 10.00hrs

A large holiday park on a hillside close to Exmouth, with spectacular views across Sandy Bay. The all-action park offers an entertainment programme for all ages throughout the day, with modern sports and leisure facilities available for everyone. An internet café is just one of the quality amenities. 43 seasonal touring pitches available. A 163 acre site with 193 touring pitches, 43 hardstandings and 1800 statics.

Leisure: **Facilities:** **Services:**

Within 3 miles:

Notes: No cars by tents. Tents only in Aug. Dogs must be kept on leads. Certain dog breeds banned. Crazy golf. Wi-fi

HOLSWORTHY

►► 75% Tamarstone Farm

Bude Rd, Pancrasweek EX22 7JT

☎ 01288 381734

e-mail: camping@tamarstone.co.uk

dir: *A30 to Launceston, then B3254 towards Bude, approx 14m. Right onto A3072 towards Holsworthy, approx 1.5m, site on left*

* £8-£10 £8-£10 £8-£10

Open Etr-end Oct Last arrival 22.00hrs Last departure noon

Four acres of river-bordered meadow and woodland providing a wildlife haven for those who enjoy peace and seclusion. The wide, sandy beaches of Bude are just five miles away, and coarse fishing is provided free on site for visitors. A 1 acre site with 16 touring pitches and 1 static.

Leisure:

Facilities:

Services:

Within 3 miles:

Notes: Dogs on leads at all times

HOLSWORTHY

► 75% Noteworthy Caravan and Campsite

Noteworthy, Bude Rd EX22 7JB

☎ 01409 253731

e-mail: enquiries@noteworthy-devon.co.uk

dir: *On A3072 between Holsworthy & Bude. 3m from Holsworthy on right*

Open all year

This campsite is owned by a friendly young couple with their own small children. There are good views from the quiet rural location, and simple toilet facilities. A 5 acre site with 5 touring pitches and 1 static.

Leisure:

Facilities:

Services:

Within 3 miles:

Notes: No open fires. Dog grooming

ILFRACOMBE

►►►► 82% Hele Valley Holiday Park

Hele Bay EX34 9RD

☎ 01271 862460 01271 867926

e-mail: holidays@helevalley.co.uk

dir: *M5 junct 27 onto A361. Through Barnstaple & Braunton to Ilfracombe. Then A399 towards Combe Martin. Follow brown Hele Valley signs. 400mtrs sharp right, then to T-junct. Reception on left*

£16-£25 £16-£25 £12-£32

Open May-Sep Last arrival 18.00hrs Last departure 11.00hrs

A deceptively spacious park set in a picturesque valley with glorious tree-lined hilly views from most pitches. High quality toilet facilities are provided, and the park is close to a lovely beach, with the harbour and other attractions of Ilfracombe just a mile away. A 17 acre site with 50 touring pitches, 12 hardstandings and 80 statics.

Leisure:

Facilities:

Services:

Within 3 miles:

Notes: No groups. Post collection, internet access, information service

KENNFORD

►►►► 76% Kennford International Caravan Park

EX6 7YN

☎ 01392 833046 🖷 01392 833046

e-mail: ian@kennfordint.fsbusiness.co.uk

web: www.kennfordinternational.co.uk

dir: *At end of M5 take A38, site signed at Kennford slip road*

Open all year (rs Winter arrival times change) Last arrival 21.00hrs Last departure 11.00hrs

Screened by trees and shrubs from the A38, this park offers many pitches divided by hedging for privacy. A high quality toilet block complements the park's facilities. A good, centrally-located base for touring the coast and countryside of Devon, and Exeter is easily accessible via the bus which stops nearby. A 15 acre site with 96 touring pitches and 53 statics.

Leisure:

Facilities:

Services:

Within 3 miles:

KENTISBEARE

►►►► 77% Forest Glade Holiday Park

Cullompton EX15 2DT

☎ 01404 841381 🖷 01404 841593

e-mail: enquiries@forest-glade.co.uk

dir: *Tent traffic: from A373 signed at Keepers Cottage Inn (2.5m E of M5 junct 28). Touring caravans: via Honiton/Dunkeswell road (please phone for access details)*

Open mid Mar-end Oct (rs Low season limited shop hours) Last arrival 21.00hrs

A quiet, attractive park in a forest clearing with well-kept gardens and beech hedge screening. One of the main attractions is the immediate proximity of the forest, which offers magnificent hillside walks with surprising views over the valleys. Please telephone for route details. A 15 acre site with 80 touring pitches, 40 hardstandings and 57 statics.

Leisure:

Facilities:

Services:

Within 3 miles:

Notes: Families & couples only. Adventure play area, paddling/ball pools, wildlife information room. Wi-fi

LYNTON

►►► 73% Lynton Camping & Caravanning Club Site

Caffyns Cross EX35 6JS

☎ 01598 752379

dir: *M5 junct 27 onto A361 to Barnstaple. Turn right to Blackmoor Gate signed Lynmouth & Lynton. Approx 5m to Caffyns Cross, immediately right to site in 1m*

Open 2 Apr-28 Sep Last arrival 21.00hrs Last departure noon

Set on high ground with excellent views over the Bristol Channel, and close to the twin resorts of Lynton & Lynmouth. This area is known as Little Switzerland because of its wooded hills, and the park is ideal for walking, and cycling on the nearby National Cycle Network. A 5.5 acre site with 105 touring pitches, 10 hardstandings.

Leisure:

Facilities:

Services:

Within 3 miles:

Notes: Site gates closed 23.00hrs-07.00hrs

MOLLAND

►►► 75% Yeo Valley Holiday Park

EX36 3NW

☎ 01769 550297

e-mail: info@yeovalleyholidays.com

dir: *From A361 onto B3227 towards Bampton. Follow brown signs for Blackcock Inn. Site opposite*

Open all year (rs Sep-Mar swimming pool closed) Last arrival 22.30hrs Last departure 10.00hrs

Set in a beautiful secluded valley on the edge of Exmoor National Park, this family-run park has easy access to both the moors and the north Devon coastline. The park is adjacent to the Blackcock Inn (under the same ownership), and has a very good heated indoor pool. A 7 acre site with 65 touring pitches, 16 hardstandings and 5 statics.

Leisure:

Facilities:

Services:

Within 3 miles:

Notes: Dogs on leads & under adult supervision

MORTEHOE

83% Twitchen House Holiday Park

Station Rd EX34 7ES

☎ 01271 870343 01271 870089

e-mail: goodtimes@woolacombe.com

dir: *From Mullacott Cross rdbt take B3343 (Woolacombe road) to Turnpike Cross junct. Take right fork, site 1.5m on left*

£15-£55 £15-£55 £10-£37

Open Mar-Oct (rs mid May & mid Sep outdoor pool closed) Last arrival mdnt Last departure 10.00hrs

A very attractive park with good leisure facilities. Visitors can use the amenities at all three of Woolacombe Bay holiday parks, and a bus service connects them all with the beach. The touring features pitches offering either sea views or a country and woodland outlook. A 45 acre site with 334 touring pitches, 110 hardstandings and 278 statics.

Leisure:

Facilities:

Services:

Within 3 miles:

Notes: Table tennis, sauna, kids' clubs, swimming & surfing lessons

MORTEHOE

►►► 85% North Morte Farm Caravan & Camping Park

North Morte Rd EX34 7EG

☎ 01271 870381 01271 870115

e-mail: info@northmortefarm.co.uk

dir: *From B3343 into Mortehoe, right at post office. Site 500yds on left*

Open Apr-Oct Last arrival 22.30hrs Last departure noon

Set in spectacular coastal countryside close to National Trust land and 500 yards from Rockham Beach. This attractive park is very well run and maintained by friendly family owners, and the quaint village of Mortehoe with its cafés, shops and pubs, is just a 5-minute walk away. A 22 acre site with 180 touring pitches, 18 hardstandings and 73 statics.

Leisure:

Facilities:

Services:

Within 3 miles:

Notes: No large groups, dogs on leads at all times

MORTEHOE

►►► 77% Easewell Farm Holiday Park & Golf Club

EX34 7EH

☎ 01271 870343 01271 870089

e-mail: goodtimes@woolacombe.com

dir: *Take B3343 to Mortehoe. Turn right at fork, site 2m on right*

£14.25-£50 £14.25-£50
£9.50-£34

Open Mar-Oct (rs Etr) Last arrival 22.00hrs Last departure 10.00hrs

A peaceful clifftop park with full-facility pitches for caravans and motorhomes, and superb views. The park offers a range of activities including indoor bowling and a 9-hole golf course, and all the facilities of the three other nearby holiday centres within this group are open to everyone. A 17 acre site with 302 touring pitches, 50 hardstandings and 1 statics.

Leisure:
Facilities:
Services:
Within 3 miles:
Notes: Snooker. Wi-fi

NEWTON ABBOT

►►►►► 95% Ross Park

Park Hill Farm, Ipplepen TQ12 5TT

☎ 01803 812983 01803 812983

e-mail: enquiries@rossparkcaravanpark.co.uk

web: www.rossparkcaravanpark.co.uk

dir: *Off A381, 3m from Newton Abbot towards Totnes, signed opposite Texaco garage towards 'Woodland'*

* £12-£23.75 £12-£23.75
£12-£23.75

Open Mar-2 Jan (rs Nov-Jan & 1st 3 wks of Mar restaurant/bar closed (ex Xmas/New Year)) Last arrival 21.00hrs Last dep 10.00hrs

A top-class park with large secluded pitches, high quality toilet facilities and floral displays throughout. The tropical conservatory also offers a breathtaking show of colour. This very rural park enjoys views of Dartmoor, and good quality meals to suit all tastes and pockets are served in the restaurant. A 32 acre site with 110 touring pitches, 94 hardstandings.

Leisure: **Facilities:** **Services:** **Within 3 miles:**
Notes: Bikes, skateboards & scooters on leisure field only. Snooker, table tennis, badminton, croquet. Wi-fi

NEWTON ABBOT

►►►►► 93% Dornafield

Dornafield Farm, Two Mile Oak TQ12 6DD

☎ 01803 812732 01803 812032

e-mail: enquiries@dornafield.com

web: www.dornafield.com

dir: *Take A381 (Newton Abbot-Totnes) for 2m. At Two Mile Oak Inn turn right, then left at x-roads in 0.5m to site on right*

Open 15 Mar-3 Jan Last arrival 22.00hrs Last departure 11.00hrs

An immaculately kept park in a tranquil wooded valley between Dartmoor and Torbay, offering either de-luxe or fully-serviced pitches. A lovely 15th-century farmhouse sits at the entrance, and the park is divided into three separate areas, served by two superb, ultra-modern toilet blocks. The friendly family owners are always available. A 30 acre site with 135 touring pitches, 97 hardstandings.

Leisure:

Facilities:

Services:

Within 3 miles:

Notes: Caravan storage (all year). Wi-fi

NEWTON ABBOT

►►► 78% Twelve Oaks Farm Caravan Park

Teigngrace TQ12 6QT

☎ 01626 352769 01626 352769

e-mail: info@twelveoaksfarm.co.uk

dir: *A38 from Exeter left signed Teigngrace (only), 0.25m before Drumbridges rdbt. 1.5m, through village, site on left. From Plymouth pass Drumbridges rdbt, take slip road for Chudleigh Knighton. Right over bridge, rejoin A38 towards Plymouth. Left for Teigngrace (only), then as above*

* £8.50-£14.50 £8.50-£14.50 £8.50-£14.50

Open all year Last arrival 21.00hrs Last departure 11.00hrs

An attractive small park on a working farm close to Dartmoor National Park, and bordered by the River Teign. The tidy pitches are located amongst trees and shrubs, and the modern facilities are very well maintained. Children will enjoy all the farm animals, and nearby is the Templar Way walking route. A 2 acre site with 35 touring pitches, 17 hardstandings.

Leisure: **Facilities:**

Services: **Within 3 miles:**

PAIGNTON

87% Beverley Parks Caravan & Camping Park

Goodrington Rd TQ4 7JE

☎ 01803 661979 01803 845427

e-mail: info@beverley-holidays.co.uk

dir: *On A380/A3022, 2m S of Paignton turn left into Goodrington Rd*

£15-£38 £15-£38 £12.50-£32

Open all year Last arrival 22.00hrs Last departure 10.00hrs

A high quality family-run park with extensive views of the bay, and plenty of on-site amenities. The park boasts indoor and outdoor heated swimming pools, and the toilet facilities are very modern and clean. The park complex is attractively laid out. 10 seasonal touring pitches available. A 12 acre site with 175 touring pitches, 36 hardstandings and 189 statics.

Leisure:

Facilities:

Services:

Within 3 miles:

Notes: No pets. Table tennis, pool, spa bath, crazy golf, sauna & gym. Wi-fi

PAIGNTON

►►►► 79% Widend Touring Park

Berry Pomeroy Rd, Marldon TQ3 1RT

☎ 01803 550116 01803 550116

dir: *Signed from Torbay ring road*

Open Apr-end Sep (rs Apr-mid May & mid Sep swimming pool & club house closed) Last arrival 20.00hrs Last departure 10.00hrs

A terraced grass park paddocked and screened on high ground overlooking Torbay with views of Dartmoor. This attractive park is well laid out, divided up by mature trees and bushes but with plenty of open grassy areas. Facilities are of a high standard and offer a heated outdoor swimming pool with sunbathing area, a small lounge bar and a well-stocked shop. A 22 acre site with 207 touring pitches, 6 hardstandings and 16 statics.

Leisure:

Facilities:

Services:

Within 3 miles:

Notes: No dogs mid Jul-Aug

PAIGNTON

►►► 84% Whitehill Country Park

Stoke Rd TQ4 7PF

☎ 01803 782338 📠 01803 782722

e-mail: info@whitehill-park.co.uk

dir: *A385 through Totnes towards Paignton. Turn right by Parkers Arms onto Stoke Rd towards Stoke Gabriel. Site on left after approx 1.5m*

£14.50-£28 £14.50-£28 £12.50-£26.50

Open Etr-Sep Last arrival 21.00hrs Last departure 10.00hrs

A family-owned and run park set in rolling countryside, with many scenic beaches just a short drive away. This extensive country park covers 40 acres with woodland walks, and plenty of flora and fauna. It offers ideal facilities, including new luxury lodges, for an excellent holiday. A 40 acre site with 260 touring pitches and 60 statics.

Leisure:

Facilities:

Services:

Within 3 miles:

Notes: No pets. Walking & cycling trails, craft room, table tennis

PAIGNTON

►►► 79% Byslades International Touring & Camping Park

Totnes Rd TQ4 7PY

☎ 01803 666930 📠 01803 555669

e-mail: info@byslades.co.uk

dir: *On A385, halfway between Paignton & Totnes*

Open Whit-Aug BH Last arrival 18.00hrs Last departure 10.00hrs

A well-kept terraced park in beautiful countryside, only two miles from Paignton. It offers a good mix of amenities, including the famous 17th-century Blagdon Inn at the adjoining holiday park home estate. There is access through to this to a full bar, snacks and restaurant service. Now owned by Haulfryn Leisure. A 23 acre site with 190 touring pitches, 40 hardstandings.

Leisure:

Facilities:

Services:

Within 3 miles:

Notes: No commercial vehicles. Crazy golf

PLYMOUTH

►►►► 79% Riverside Caravan Park

Longbridge Rd PL6 8LL

☎ 01752 344122 📠 01752 344122

e-mail: info@riversidecaravanpark.com

dir: *A38 follow signs at Marsh Mills rdbt, take 3rd exit, then left. 400yds turn right (keep River Plym on right) to site*

Open all year (rs Oct-Etr bar, restaurant & take-away closed) Last arrival 22.00hrs Last departure 10.00hrs

A well-groomed site on the outskirts of Plymouth on the banks of the River Plym, in a quiet location surrounded by woodland. The toilet facilities are to a very good standard, and include private cubicles. This park is an ideal stopover for the ferries to France and Spain, and makes an excellent base for touring Dartmoor and the coast. An 11 acre site with 293 touring pitches.

Leisure:

Facilities:

Services:

Within 3 miles:

SALCOMBE

►►► 78% Higher Rew Caravan & Camping Park

Higher Rew, Malborough TQ7 3BW

☎ 01548 842681 📠 01548 843681

e-mail: enquiries@higherrew.co.uk

dir: *A381 to Malborough. Right at Townsend Cross, follow signs to Soar for 1m. Left at Rew Cross*

* £11-£17 £11-£17 £10-£15

Open Etr-Oct Last arrival 22.00hrs Last departure noon

A long-established park in a remote location in sight of the sea. The spacious, open touring field has some tiered pitches in the sloping grass, and there are lovely countryside or sea views from every pitch. Friendly family owners are continually improving the facilities. A 5 acre site with 85 touring pitches.

Leisure:

Facilities:

Services:

Within 3 miles:

Notes: Play barn

SHALDON

76%

Coast View Holiday Park

Torquay Rd TQ14 0BG

☎ 01626 872392 01626 872719

e-mail: info@coastview.co.uk

dir: *M5 junct 31, A38 then A380 towards Torquay. Then A381 towards Teignmouth. Right in 4m at lights, over Shaldon Bridge. 0.75m, up hill, site on right*

Open 15 Mar-1 Nov Last arrival 21.00hrs Last departure 10.30hrs

This park has stunning sea views from its spacious pitches. The family-run park has a full entertainment programme every night for all the family, plus outdoor and indoor activities for children, and will appeal to lively families. A 17 acre site with 110 touring pitches, 6 hardstandings and 86 statics.

Leisure:
Facilities:
Services:
Within 3 miles:
Notes: Crazy golf, assault course, indoor soft play areas. Wi-fi

SIDMOUTH

►►►►► 82%

Oakdown Holiday Park

Gatedown Ln, Weston EX10 0PT

☎ 01297 680387 01297 680541

e-mail: enquiries@oakdown.co.uk

web: www.oakdown.co.uk

dir: *Off A3052, 2.5m E of junct with A375*

£13.35-£26.50 £13.35-£26.50 £11.20-£21.25

Open Apr-Oct Last arrival 22.00hrs Last departure 10.30hrs

A friendly, well-maintained park with good landscaping and plenty of maturing trees, well screened from the road. Pitches are grouped in paddocks surrounded by shrubs. A new 50-pitch development has an upmarket toilet block. Conservation areas offer attractive walks, and there is a hide for bird watchers by the reed bed. A 16 acre site with 150 touring pitches, 90 hardstandings and 62 statics.

Leisure: **Facilities:** **Services:**
Within 3 miles:
Notes: Dogs must be kept on leads. No bikes, skateboards or kite flying. Use of microwave. Wi-fi

SIDMOUTH

►►► 76% Kings Down Tail Caravan & Camping Park

Salcombe Regis EX10 0PD

☎ 01297 680313 📠 01297 680313

e-mail: info@kingsdowntail.co.uk

dir: *Off A3052 3m E of junct with A375*

* £15-£17 £15-£17 £12-£14

Open 15 Mar-15 Nov Last arrival 22.00hrs Last departure noon

A well-kept site on level ground in a tree-sheltered spot on the side of the Sid Valley. This neat family-run park makes a good base for exploring the east Devon coast. A 5 acre site with 100 touring pitches, 51 hardstandings.

Leisure:

Facilities:

Services:

Within 3 miles:

Notes: Dogs must be kept on leads at all times. Wet room for disabled or family use

SLAPTON

►►► 77% Slapton Sands Camping & Caravanning Club Site

Middle Grounds TQ7 2QW

☎ 01548 580538

dir: *On A379 from Kingsbridge. Site entrance 0.25m from A379, beyond brow of hill approaching Slapton*

Open 2 Apr-2 Nov Last arrival 21.00hrs Last departure noon

A very attractive location and well-run site overlooking Start Bay, with extensive views from some pitches, and glimpses of the sea from others. The shingle beach of Slapton Sands, and the Blue Flag beach at Blackpool Sands are among attractions, along with a nearby freshwater lake and nature reserve. A 5.5 acre site with 115 touring pitches, 10 hardstandings.

Leisure:

Facilities:

Services:

Within 3 miles:

Notes: Members' touring caravans only. Site gates closed 23.00hrs-07.00hrs

STOKENHAM

►►► 79% Old Cotmore Farm

TQ7 2LR

☎ 01548 580240

e-mail: info@holiday-in-devon.com

dir: *From Kingsbridge take A379 towards Dartmouth, through Frogmore & Chillington to mini rdbt at Stokenham. Right towards Beesands, site 1m on right*

* £11-£18 £11-£18 £11-£18

Open 15 Mar-Oct Last arrival 20.00hrs Last departure 11.00hrs

A small and peaceful, family-run touring caravan and camp site well located in the South Hams, close to Slapton and within easy reach of Salcombe and Dartmouth. Facilities are very clean and well maintained and there is a basic shop and small play area. Pebble and sandy beaches with cliff walks through woods and fields are within walking distance. Self-catering cottages are available. A 22 acre site with 30 touring pitches, 25 hardstandings.

Leisure:

Facilities:

Services:

Within 3 miles:

Notes: Wi-fi

TAVISTOCK

►►►► 84% Woodovis Park

Gulworthy PL19 8NY

☎ 01822 832968 01822 832948

e-mail: info@woodovis.com

dir: *A390 from Tavistock signed Callington & Gunnislake. At hill top right at rdbt signed Lamerton & Chipshop. Site 1m on left*

* £18-£32 £18-£32 £18-£32

Open 27 Mar-30 Oct Last arrival 22.00hrs Last departure noon

A well-kept park in a remote woodland setting on the edge of the Tamar Valley. This peacefully-located park is set at the end of a half-mile private tree-lined road, and has lots of on-site facilities. The toilets are excellent, and there is an indoor swimming pool, all in a friendly, purposeful atmosphere. A 14.5 acre site with 50 touring pitches, 24 hardstandings and 35 statics.

Leisure:

Facilities:

Services:

Within 3 miles:

Notes: Dogs must be kept on leads. Mini golf, sauna, jacuzzi, archery & water-walking. Wi-fi

TAVISTOCK

►►► 83% Langstone Manor Camping & Caravan Park

Moortown PL19 9JZ

☎ 01822 613371 01822 613371

e-mail: jane@langstone-manor.co.uk

web: www.langstone-manor.co.uk

dir: *Take B3357 from Tavistock to Princetown. Approx 1.5m turn right at x-rds, follow signs*

* £12-£15 £12-£15 £12-£15

Open 15 Mar-Oct (rs Wkdys in low season restricted hours in bar & restaurant) Last arrival 22.00hrs Last departure 11.00hrs

A secluded site set in the well-maintained grounds of a manor house in Dartmoor National Park. Many attractive mature trees provide a screen within the park, and there is a popular lounge bar with an excellent menu of reasonably priced evening meals. Plenty of activities and places of interest can be found within the surrounding moorland. A 6.5 acre site with 40 touring pitches, 10 hardstandings and 25 statics.

Leisure: **Facilities:** **Services:** **Within 3 miles:** **Notes:** No skateboards, scooters, cycles or ball games

TAVISTOCK

►►► 80% Harford Bridge Holiday Park

Peter Tavy PL19 9LS

☎ 01822 810349 01822 810028

e-mail: enquiry@harfordbridge.co.uk

web: www.harfordbridge.co.uk

dir: *2m N of Tavistock, off A386 Okehampton Rd, take Peter Tavy turn, entrance 200yds on right*

* £11.50-£19.80 £11.50-£19.80 £11.50-£18.50

Open end Mar-mid Nov Last arrival 21.00hrs Last departure noon

This beautiful spacious park is set beside the River Tavy in the Dartmoor National Park. Pitches are located beside the river and around the copses, and the park is very well equipped for the holidaymaker. An adventure playground and games room entertain children, and there is fly-fishing and a free tennis court. A 16 acre site with 120 touring pitches, 5 hardstandings and 80 statics.

Leisure:

Facilities:

Services:

Within 3 miles:

Notes: No large groups. Wi-fi

TEDBURN ST MARY

►►►► 78% Springfield Holiday Park

EX6 6EW

☎ 01647 24242

e-mail: enquiries@springfieldholidaypark.co.uk

dir: *M5 junct 31, A30 towards Okehampton, exit at junct, signed to Cheriton Bishop. Follow brown tourist signs to site*

£12-£20 £12-£20 £10-£20

Open 15 Mar-15 Nov Last arrival 22.00hrs Last departure noon

Set in a quiet rural location with countryside views, this park continues to be upgraded to a smart standard. It has the advantage of being located close to Dartmoor National Park, with village pubs and stores just two miles away. 38 seasonal touring pitches are available. A 9 acre site with 48 touring pitches, 38 hardstandings and 49 statics.

Leisure:

Facilities:

Services:

Within 3 miles:

Notes: Dogs must be kept on leads. Family shower rooms

UMBERLEIGH

►►► 75% Umberleigh Camping & Caravanning Club Site

Over Weir EX37 9DU

☎ 01769 560009

dir: *On A377 from Barnstaple turn right at Umberleigh sign onto B3227. Site on right in 0.25m*

Open 2 Apr-2 Nov Last arrival 21.00hrs Last departure noon

There are fine country views from this compact site set on high ground. The site has the advantage of a games room with table tennis and skittle alley, and two quality tennis courts, with an adjacent wooded area for walks, and a nearby fishing pond. A 3 acre site with 60 touring pitches, 12 hardstandings.

Leisure:

Facilities:

Services:

Within 3 miles:

Notes: Site gates closed 23.00hrs-07.00hrs

WOODBURY SALTERTON

►►► 86% Browns Farm Caravan Park

Browns Farm EX5 1PS

☎ 01395 232895

dir: *M5 junct 30, A3052 for 3.7m. Right at White Horse Inn follow sign to Woodbury, at village road junct turn right, site on left*

* £10-£13 £10-£13 £10-£13

Open all year Last departure 11.00hrs

A small farm park adjoining a 14th-century thatched farmhouse, and located in a quiet village. Pitches back onto hedgerows, and friendly owners keep the facilities very clean. The tourist information and games room with table tennis, chess etc is housed in a purpose-built building. The park is just a mile from the historic heathland of Woodbury Common with its superb views. A 2.5 acre site with 29 touring pitches, 24 hardstandings.

Leisure:

Facilities:

Services:

Within 3 miles:

Notes: No ground sheets in awnings, no music. Hardstandings for winter period, caravan storage

WOOLACOMBE

80% Woolacombe Bay Holiday Village

Sandy Ln EX34 7AH

☎ 01271 870343 01271 870089

e-mail: goodtimes@woolacombe.com

dir: *From Mullacott Cross rdbt take B3343 (Woolacombe road) to Turnpike Cross junct. Right towards Mortehoe, site approx 1m on left*

£10-£37

Open Mar-Oct (rs Mar-mid May, mid Sep-Oct no touring, camping only available) Last arrival mdnt Last departure 10.00hrs

A well-developed touring section in a holiday complex with a full entertainment and leisure programme. This park offers excellent facilities including steam room and sauna. For a small charge a bus takes holidaymakers to the other Woolacombe Bay holiday centres, and there is also a bus to the beach. An 8.5 acre site with 180 touring pitches and 237 statics.

Leisure:

Facilities:

Services:

Within 3 miles:

Notes: Entertainment, kids' club, health suite, surfing & swimming lessons

WOOLACOMBE

76% Golden Coast Holiday Park

Station Rd EX34 7HW

☎ 01271 870343 01271 870089

e-mail: goodtimes@woolacombe.com

dir: *From Mullacott Cross towards Woolacombe Bay, site 1.5m on left*

£15-£55 £15-£55 £10-£37

Open Feb-Dec (rs mid Sep-May outdoor pools closed) Last arrival mdnt Last departure 10.00hrs

A holiday village offering excellent leisure facilities as well as the amenities of the other Woolacombe Bay holiday parks. There is a neat touring area with a unisex toilet block, maintained to a high standard. Bowling alleys, a number of bars and plenty of activities add to the holiday experience. A 10 acre site with 91 touring pitches, 53 hardstandings and 444 statics.

Leisure:
Facilities:
Services:
Within 3 miles:
Notes: Sauna, solarium, golf, fishing, snooker, cinema, kids' clubs, swimming & surfing lessons. Wi-fi

WOOLACOMBE

76% Woolacombe Sands Holiday Park

Beach Rd EX34 7AF

☎ 01271 870569 01271 870606

e-mail: lifesabeach@woolacombe-sands.co.uk

dir: *M5 junct 27, A361 to Barnstaple. Follow Ilfracombe signs, until Mullacott Cross. Turn left onto B3343 to Woolacombe. Site on left*

Open Apr-Oct Last arrival 22.00hrs Last departure 10.00hrs

Set in rolling countryside with grassy terraced pitches, most with spectacular views overlooking the sea at Woolacombe. The lovely Blue Flag beach can be accessed directly by footpath in 10-15 minutes, and there is a full entertainment programme for all the family in high season. A 20 acre site with 200 touring pitches and 80 statics.

Leisure:
Facilities:
Services:
Within 3 miles:
Notes: Kids' club

WOOLACOMBE

►►► 77% Europa Park

Beach Rd EX34 7AN

☎ 01271 871425 🖹 01271 871425

e-mail: europaparkwoolacombe@yahoo.co.uk

dir: *M5 junct 27, A361 through Barnstaple to Mullacott Cross. Left onto B3343 signed Woolacombe. Site on right at Spa shop & garage*

Open all year Last arrival 23.00hrs

A very lively family-run site handy for the beach at Woolacombe, and catering well for surfers but maybe not suitable for a quieter type of stay (please check the site is suitable for you before making your booking). Set in a stunning location high above the bay, it provides a wide range of accommodation including surf cabins, and generous touring pitches. Visitors can enjoy the indoor pool and sauna, games room, restaurant/café/bar and clubhouse. A 16 acre site with 200 touring pitches, 20 hardstandings and 22 statics.

Leisure: **Facilities:** **Services:** **Within 3 miles:**

Notes: Beer deck, off licence, pub, big-screen TV

ALDERHOLT

►►►► 84% Hill Cottage Farm Camping and Caravan Park

Sandleheath Rd SP6 3EG

☎ 01425 650513 🖹 01425 652339

e-mail: hillcottagefarmcaravansite@supanet.com

dir: *Take B3078 W of Fordingbridge. Turn off at Alderholt, site 0.25m on left after railway bridge*

Open Mar-Nov Last arrival 19.00hrs Last departure 11.00hrs

Set within extensive grounds this rural, beautifully landscaped park offers all fully-serviced pitches set in individual hardstanding bays with mature hedges between giving adequate pitch privacy. A modern toilet block is kept immaculately clean, and there's a good range of leisure facilities. In high season there is an area available for tenting. A 40 acre site with 35 touring pitches, 35 hardstandings.

Leisure:

Facilities:

Services:

Within 3 miles:

Notes: Wi-fi

BERE REGIS

►►► 80%
Rowlands Wait Touring Park

Rye Hill BH20 7LP

☎ 01929 472727 01929 472275

e-mail: enquiries@rowlandswait.co.uk

web: www.rowlandswait.co.uk

dir: *On approach to Bere Regis follow signs to Bovington Tank Museum. At top of Rye Hill, 0.75m from village turn right. 200yds to site*

* £14-£18 £14-£18 £12-£15

Open mid Mar-Oct (winter by arrangement) Last arrival 21.30hrs Last departure noon

This park lies in a really attractive setting overlooking Bere Regis and the Dorset countryside, set amongst undulating areas of trees and shrubs. The toilet facilities include two family rooms. Within a few miles of the Tank Museum with its mock battles. 20 seasonal touring pitches available. An 8 acre site with 71 touring pitches, 2 hardstandings.

Leisure:

Facilities:

Services:

Within 3 miles:

Notes: No open fires

BLANDFORD FORUM

►►►► 77% The Inside Park

Down House Estate DT11 9AD

☎ 01258 453719 01258 459921

e-mail: inspark@aol.com

dir: *From town, over River Stour, follow Winterborne Stickland signs. Site in 1.5m*

£14-£21 £14-£21 £14-£21

Open Etr-Oct Last arrival 22.00hrs Last departure noon

An attractive, well-sheltered and quiet park, half a mile off a country lane in a wooded valley. Spacious pitches are divided by mature trees and shrubs, and amenities are housed in an 18th-century coach house and stables. There are some lovely woodland walks within the park. A 12 acre site with 125 touring pitches.

Leisure:

Facilities:

Services:

Within 3 miles:

Notes: Farm trips (main season). Kennels for hire

BRIDPORT

85% Freshwater Beach Holiday Park

Burton Bradstock DT6 4PT

☎ 01308 897317 01308 897336

e-mail: office@freshwaterbeach.co.uk

web: www.freshwaterbeach.co.uk

dir: *Take B3157 from Bridport towards Burton Bradstock. Site 1.5m from Crown rdbt on right*

* £13-£37 £13-£37 £13-£37

Open 15 Mar-10 Nov Last arrival 22.00hrs Last departure 10.00hrs

A family holiday centre sheltered by a sandbank and enjoying its own private beach. The park offers a wide variety of leisure and entertainment programmes for all the family. It is well placed at one end of the Weymouth/Bridport coast with spectacular views of Chesil Beach. There are three immaculate toilet blocks. A 40 acre site with 500 touring pitches and 250 statics.

Leisure: **Facilities:** **Services:**

Within 3 miles:

Notes: Families & couples only. Large TV, internet, entertainment

BRIDPORT

81% West Bay Holiday Park

West Bay DT6 4HB

☎ 0844 335 3756 01308 421371

e-mail: touringandcamping@parkdeanholidays.com

web: www.parkdeantouring.com

dir: *From A35 (Dorchester road), W towards Bridport, take 1st exit at 1st rdbt, 2nd exit at 2nd rdbt into West Bay, site on right*

* £12-£42 £12-£42 £12-£42

Open Mar-Oct Last arrival 21.00hrs Last departure 10.00hrs

Overlooking the pretty little harbour at West Bay, and close to the shingle beach, this park offers a full entertainment programme for all ages. There are children's clubs and an indoor pool with flume for all the family, and plenty of evening fun with talent shows and cabaret etc. The grassy touring area is terraced to enjoy the seaward views. A large adventure playground is very popular. A 6 acre site with 131 touring pitches, 10 hardstandings and 307 statics.

Leisure: **Facilities:** **Services:** **Within 3 miles:**

Notes: No skateboards. Wi-fi

BRIDPORT

►►►►► 86% Highlands End Holiday Park

Eype DT6 6AR

☎ 01308 422139 & 426947

01308 425672

e-mail: holidays@wdlh.co.uk

dir: *1m W of Bridport on A35, turn south for Eype. Site signed*

Open mid Mar-early Nov Last arrival 22.00hrs Last departure 11.00hrs

A well-screened site with magnificent clifftop views over the Channel and Dorset coast, adjacent to National Trust land and overlooking Lyme Bay. Pitches are mostly sheltered by hedging and well spaced on hardstandings. There is a mixture of statics and tourers, but the tourers enjoy the best clifftop positions. A 9 acre site with 195 touring pitches, 45 hardstandings and 160 statics.

Leisure: **Facilities:** **Services:** **Within 3 miles:**

Notes: Gym, steam room, sauna, pitch & putt, tourist information. Wi-fi

CHARMOUTH

►►►►► 85% Wood Farm Caravan & Camping Park

Axminster Rd DT6 6BT

☎ 01297 560697 01297 561243

e-mail: holidays@woodfarm.co.uk

web: www.woodfarm.co.uk

dir: *Site entered directly off A35 rdbt, on Axminster side of Charmouth*

* £4.85-£11.75 £4.85-£11.75 £4.85-£11.75

Open Etr-Oct Last arrival 19.00hrs Last departure noon

A pleasant, well-established and mature park overlooking Charmouth, the sea and the Dorset hills and valleys. It stands on a high spot, and the four camping fields are terraced, each with its own toilet block. Convenient for Lyme Regis, Axminster, and the famous fossil coastline. 20 seasonal touring pitches available. A 13 acre site with 216 touring pitches, 175 hardstandings and 81 statics.

Leisure: **Facilities:** **Services:** **Within 3 miles:**

Notes: No skateboards, scooters or roller skates. Coarse fishing lake. Wi-fi

CHARMOUTH

►►►► 85% Newlands Caravan & Camping Park

DT6 6RB

☎ 01297 560259 📠 01297 560787

e-mail: enq@newlandsholidays.co.uk

web: www.newlandsholidays.co.uk

dir: *4m W of Bridport on A35*

Open 10 Mar-4 Nov Last arrival 22.30hrs Last departure 10.00hrs

A very smart site with excellent touring facilities. The park offers a full cabaret and entertainment programme for all ages, and boasts an indoor swimming pool with spa and an outdoor pool with water slide. Set on gently sloping ground in hilly countryside near the sea. A 23 acre site with 240 touring pitches, 52 hardstandings and 86 statics.

Leisure:

Facilities:

Services:

Within 3 miles:

Notes: Wi-fi

CHARMOUTH

►►► 80% Manor Farm Holiday Centre

DT6 6QL

☎ 01297 560226

e-mail: enq@manorfarmholidaycentre.co.uk

dir: *W on A35 to Charmouth, site 0.75m on right*

* £12-£24 £12-£24 £12-£24

Open all year (rs End Oct-mid Mar statics only) Last arrival 20.00hrs Last departure 10.00hrs

Set just a short walk from the safe sand and shingle beach at Charmouth, this popular family park offers a good range of facilities. Children enjoy the activity area and outdoor swimming pool (so do their parents!), and the park also offers a lively programme in the extensive bar and entertainment complex. 100 seasonal touring pitches available. A 30 acre site with 400 touring pitches, 80 hardstandings and 29 statics.

Leisure:

Facilities:

Services:

Within 3 miles:

Notes: No skateboards. Wi-fi

CHIDEOCK

►►►► 82% Golden Cap Holiday Park

Seatown DT6 6JX

☎ 01308 422139 & 426947

01308 425672

e-mail: holidays@wdlh.co.uk

dir: *On A35, in Chideock turn S for Seatown, site signed*

Open mid Mar-early Nov Last arrival 22.00hrs Last departure 11.00hrs

A grassy site, overlooking sea and beach and surrounded by National Trust parkland. This uniquely placed park slopes down to the sea, although pitches are generally level. A slight dip hides the beach view from the back of the park, but this area benefits from having trees, scrub and meadows, unlike the barer areas closer to the sea. Ideal base for touring Dorset and Devon. An 11 acre site with 108 touring pitches, 24 hardstandings and 234 statics.

Leisure:

Facilities:

Services:

Within 3 miles:

Notes: Fishing lake, tourist information. Wi-fi

CHRISTCHURCH

►►►► 88% Grove Farm Meadow Holiday Caravan Park

Stour Way BH23 2PQ

☎ 01202 483597 01202 483878

e-mail: enquiries@meadowbank-holidays.co.uk

web: www.meadowbank-holidays.co.uk

dir: *A31 onto A338 towards Bournemouth. Take 1st exit after 5m then left towards Christchurch on B3073. Right at 1st rdbt into St Catherine's Way/River Way. Stour Way 3rd right, site at end of road*

Open Mar-Oct Last arrival 21.00hrs Last departure noon

A smart park on the banks of the Stour, with a fine display of hanging baskets and flower-filled tubs around the reception area. Toilet facilities are modern, and there's excellent play equipment for the kids. Visitors can choose between pitch sizes, including fully-serviced ones. A 2 acre site with 41 touring pitches, 22 hardstandings and 180 statics.

Leisure: **Facilities:** **Services:** **Within 3 miles:** **Notes:** No tents. No pets. Fishing on site

CORFE CASTLE

►►► 79% Corfe Castle Camping & Caravanning Club Site

Bucknowle BH20 5PQ

☎ 01929 480280

dir: *From Wareham A351 towards Swanage. In 4m turn right at foot of Corfe Castle signed Church Knowle. 0.75m right to site*

Open Mar-Oct Last arrival 20.00hrs Last departure noon

A quiet family park set in a clearing within a wooded area, with touring pitches spread around the perimeter in secluded areas. The central grass area is kept free as a play space, and there are many walks from the park. The park is now franchised to the Camping & Caravanning Club. A 5 acre site with 80 touring pitches.

Leisure:

Facilities:

Services:

Notes: Site gates closed between 23.00hrs-07.00hrs

HOLTON HEATH

82% Sandford Holiday Park

Organford Rd BH16 6JZ

☎ 0844 335 3756 📠 01202 625678

e-mail: touringandcamping@parkdeanholidays.com

web: www.parkdeantouring.com

dir: *A35 from Poole towards Dorchester, at lights onto A351 towards Wareham. Right at Holton Heath. Site 100yds on left*

* £12-£40 £12-£40 £12-£40

Open Mar-Nov (rs 17 May-6 Sep outdoor pool open) Last arrival 22.00hrs Last dep 10.00hrs

With touring pitches set in 20 acres surrounded by woodland, this park offers a full range of leisure activities and is neat and well maintained. Children's clubs in the daytime and nightly entertainment. A reception area with lounge, bar, café and restaurant, and a covered area outside with tables and chairs in well landscaped gardens. A 64 acre site with 354 touring pitches and 344 statics.

Leisure: **Facilities:** **Services:** **Within 3 miles:** **Notes:** Bowling, family entertainment, crazy golf, bike hire, adventure playground, amusements. Wi-fi

LYME REGIS

►►►► 82%

Shrubbery Touring Park

Rousdon DT7 3XW

☎ 01297 442227 01297 446086

e-mail: enq@shrubberypark.co.uk

web: www.shrubberypark.co.uk

dir: *3m W of Lyme Regis on A3052 (coast road)*

£10.25-£15.25 £10.25-£15.25
£10.25-£15.25

Open mid Mar-Oct Last arrival 22.00hrs Last departure 11.00hrs

Mature trees enclose this peaceful park which has distant views of the lovely countryside. The modern facilities are well kept, and there is plenty of space for children to play in the grounds. Located on the Devon/Dorset border, just three miles from Lyme Regis. A 10 acre site with 120 touring pitches, 10 hardstandings.

Leisure:

Facilities:

Services:

Within 3 miles:

Notes: No motor scooters, roller skates or skateboards. No groups (except rallies). Crazy golf

LYTCHETT MINSTER

►►►►► 80%

South Lytchett Manor

Dorchester Rd BH16 6JB

☎ 01202 622577

e-mail: info@southlytchettmanor.co.uk

dir: *On B3067, off A35, 1m E of Lytchett Minster, 600yds on right after village*

* £16.50-£22.75 £16.50-£22.75
£14.50-£22.75

Open Mar-2 Jan Last arrival 21.00hrs Last departure 11.00hrs

Situated in the grounds of a historic Manor House the park has new and modern facilities which are spotless and well maintained. This lovely park is well located for visiting Poole and Bournemouth, and the Jurassic X53 bus route runs from just outside the park and along the coast. 20 seasonal touring pitches available. A 20 acre site with 150 touring pitches, 38 hardstandings.

Leisure:

Facilities:

Services:

Within 3 miles:

Notes: No camp fires. 2 family bathrooms. Internet access. Wi-fi

ORGANFORD

►►►► 80%

Pear Tree Holiday Park

Organford Rd, Holton Heath BH16 6LA

☎ 01202 622434

e-mail: enquiries@peartreepark.co.uk

web: www.peartreepark.co.uk

dir: *From Poole take A35 towards Dorchester, onto A351 towards Wareham, at 1st lights turn right, site 300yds on left*

Open Mar-Oct Last arrival 19.00hrs Last departure 10.00hrs

A quiet, sheltered country park, with refurbished toilet facilities offering quality and comfort. The touring area is divided into terraces with mature hedges for screening, with a separate level tenting area on the edge of woodland. A bridle path leads into Wareham Forest. A 9 acre site with 154 touring pitches, 82 hardstandings and 40 statics.

Leisure:

Facilities:

Services:

Within 3 miles:

Notes: Wi-fi

OWERMOIGNE

►►► 77%

Sandyholme Holiday Park

Moreton Rd DT2 8HZ

☎ 01308 422139 & 426947

e-mail: sandyholme@wdlh.co.uk

web: www.wdlh.co.uk

dir: *From A352 (Wareham to Dorchester road) turn right to Owermoigne for 1m. Site on left*

Open 20 Mar-8 Nov (rs Etr) Last arrival 22.00hrs Last departure 11.00hrs

A pleasant site in a tree-lined rural setting within easy reach of the coast at Lulworth Cove, and handy for several seaside resorts. The facilities are very good, including a superb toilet block, and good food is available in the lounge/bar. A 6 acre site with 46 touring pitches and 52 statics.

Leisure:

Facilities:

Services:

Within 3 miles:

Notes: Table tennis, wildlife lake, tourist information

POOLE

80% Rockley Park

Hamworthy BH15 4LZ

☎ 01202 679393 01202 683159

e-mail: rockley-holidays@bourne-leisure.co.uk

dir: *Take A31 off M27 to Poole centre, then follow signs to site*

* £16-£92 £16-£92 £20-£68

Open mid Mar-Oct (rs mid Mar-May & Sep-Oct some facilities may be reduced) Last departure 10.00hrs

A complete holiday experience including a wide range of day and night entertainment, and plenty of sports and leisure activities. Water sports are comprehensively covered, and there is also mooring and launching from the park. The touring area provides good quality facilities. A 90 acre site with 71 touring pitches, 71 hardstandings and 1077 statics.

Leisure:

Facilities:

Services:

Within 3 miles:

Notes: No cars by tents. Dogs not allowed during peak periods or on touring pitches. Tents only from May-Sep. Sailing school. Wi-fi

POOLE

►►► 77% Beacon Hill Touring Park

Blandford Road North BH16 6AB

☎ 01202 631631 01202 624388

e-mail: bookings@beaconhilltouringpark.co.uk

dir: *On A350, 0.25m N of junct with A35, 3m NW of Poole*

* £10-£25 £10-£25 £8.50-£25

Open Etr-end Oct (rs Low & mid season some services closed/restricted opening) Last arrival 23.00hrs Last departure 11.00hrs

Set in an attractive, wooded area with conservation very much in mind. Two large ponds for coarse fishing are within the grounds and the terraced pitches, informally sited so that visitors can choose their favourite spot, offer some fine views. The excellent outdoor swimming pool and tennis court are popular during the summer period. A 30 acre site with 170 touring pitches, 10 hardstandings.

Leisure: **Facilities:** **Services:** **Within 3 miles:**

Notes: Groups of young people not accepted during high season. Wi-fi

PORTESHAM

►►►► 78% Portesham Dairy Farm Campsite

Weymouth DT3 4HG

☎ 01305 871297

e-mail: info@porteshamdairyfarm.co.uk

dir: *From Dorchester on A35 towards Bridport. After 5m left at Winterbourne Abbas, follow Portesham signs. Through village, left at Kings Arms pub, site in 350yds on right*

* £10-£24 £10-£24 £10-£24

Open mid Mar-Oct Last arrival 22.00hrs Last departure 16.00hrs

Located at the edge of the picturesque village of Portesham, this family run park is part of a small working farm in a quiet rural location. This level park has a local pub near the site entrance where meals are served, and with a garden for children. Seasonal touring pitches are available. An 8 acre site with 90 touring pitches, 61 hardstandings.

Leisure:

Facilities:

Services:

Within 3 miles:

Notes: No commercial vehicles. Fully serviced pitches, caravan storage

ST LEONARDS

►►►► 91% Shamba Holidays

230 Ringwood Rd BH24 2SB

☎ 01202 873302 01202 873392

e-mail: enquiries@shambaholidays.co.uk

web: www.shambaholidays.co.uk

dir: *Off A31, from Poole turn left into Eastmoors Lane, 100yds past 2nd rdbt from Texaco garage. Site 0.25m on right (just past Woodman Inn)*

* £18-£28 £18-£28 £18-£28

Open Mar-Oct (rs Low season some facilities only open at wknds) Last arrival 22.00hrs Last departure 11.00hrs

A relaxed touring park in pleasant countryside between the New Forest and Bournemouth. The park is very well equipped for holidaymakers, with swimming pool, good playground, and bar, shop and takeaway. A 7 acre site with 150 touring pitches.

Leisure:

Facilities:

Services:

Within 3 miles:

Notes: No large groups, no commercial vehicles. Phone card top-up facility, playing field

ST LEONARDS

►►► 78% Forest Edge Touring Park

229 Ringwood Rd BH24 2SD

☎ 01590 648331 01590 645610

e-mail: holidays@shorefield.co.uk

dir: *From E: on A31 over 1st rdbt (Little Chef), pass St Leonards Hotel, left at next rdbt into Boundary Ln, site 100yds on left. From W: on A31 pass Texaco garage & Woodsman Inn, right at rdbt into Boundary Ln*

Open Feb-3 Jan (rs School & summer hols pool open) Last arrival 21.00hrs Last dep 10.00hrs

A tree-lined park set in grassland with plenty of excellent amenities for all the family, including an outdoor heated swimming pool and toddlers' pool, an adventure playground, and two launderettes. Visitors may also use the leisure club and all amenities at the sister site of Oakdene Forest Park nearby. Some pitches may experience traffic noise from the nearby A31. A 9 acre site with 92 touring pitches and 28 statics.

Leisure: **Facilities:** **Services:** **Within 3 miles:** **Notes:** Families & couples only. Rallies welcome. 1 dog & car per pitch

SIXPENNY HANDLEY

►►►► 80% Church Farm Caravan & Camping Park

The Bungalow, Church Farm High St SP5 5ND

☎ 01725 553005 & 552563

e-mail: churchfarmcandcpark@yahoo.co.uk

dir: *1m S of Handley Hill rdbt. Turn off for Sixpenny Handley, right by school, site 300yds by church*

£6.50-£7.50 £6.50-£7.50 £6.50-£7.50

Open all year (rs Nov-Mar 10 vans) Last arrival 21.00hrs Last departure anytime

A spacious, open park located within Cranborne Chase in an Area of Outstanding Natural Beauty. Ongoing improvements have seen the completion of new facility block with good private toilet facilities, and a café/restaurant. The village of Sixpenny Handley is 200yds away. A 10 acre site with 35 touring pitches, 2 hardstandings and 2 statics.

Leisure:

Facilities:

Services:

Within 3 miles:

Notes: Dogs must be kept on leads, quiet after 23.00hrs. Recycling facilities, caravan storage. Wi-fi

SWANAGE

►►► 80% Ulwell Cottage Caravan Park

Ulwell Cottage, Ulwell BH19 3DG

☎ 01929 422823 01929 421500

e-mail: enq@ulwellcottagepark.co.uk

web: www.ulwellcottagepark.co.uk

dir: *From Swanage N for 2m on unclass road towards Studland*

* £12-£40 £12-£40 £12-£40

Open Mar-7 Jan (rs Mar-Spring BH & mid Sep-early Jan takeaway closed, shop open variable hrs) Last arrival 22.00hrs Last departure 11.00hrs

Nestling under the Purbeck Hills surrounded by scenic walks and only two miles from the beach. This family-run park caters well for families and couples, offering high quality facilities including an indoor heated swimming pool and village inn. A 13 acre site with 77 touring pitches, 19 hardstandings and 140 statics.

Leisure:

Facilities:

Services:

Within 3 miles:

Notes: Wi-fi

SWANAGE

►►► 77% Herston Caravan & Camping Park

Washpond Ln BH19 3DJ

☎ 01929 422932 01929 423888

e-mail: office@herstonleisure.co.uk

dir: *From Wareham on A351 towards Swanage. Washpond Ln on left just after 'Welcome to Swanage' sign*

£20-£40 £20-£40 £15-£30

Open all year

Set in a rural area with extensive views of the Purbecks, this tree lined park has many full facility pitches and quality toilet facilities. Herston Halt is within walking distance, a stop for the famous Swanage steam railway between the town centre and Corfe Castle. A 10 acre site with 100 touring pitches, 71 hardstandings and 5 statics.

Facilities:

Services:

Within 3 miles:

Notes: No noise after 23.00hrs. Dogs to be kept on leads. Wi-fi

VERWOOD

►►► 75% Verwood Camping & Caravanning Club Site

Sutton Hill, Woodlands BH21 8NQ

☎ 01202 822763

dir: *13m from Salisbury turn left from A354 onto B3081. Site 1.5m W of Verwood*

Open 2 Apr-2 Nov Last arrival 21.00hrs Last departure noon

Set on rising ground between the woodland of the New Forest and the rolling downs of Cranborne Chase and Salisbury Plains. This comfortable site is well kept by very keen wardens. A 12.7 acre site with 150 touring pitches, 18 hardstandings.

Leisure:

Facilities:

Services:

Within 3 miles:

Notes: Site gates closed 23.00hrs-07.00hrs

WAREHAM

►►►►► 84% Wareham Forest Tourist Park

North Trigon BH20 7NZ

☎ 01929 551393 01929 558321

e-mail: holiday@warehamforest.co.uk

dir: *Telephone for directions*

Open all year (rs Off-peak season limited services) Last arrival 21.00hrs Last departure 11.00hrs

A woodland park within the tranquil Wareham Forest, with its many walks and proximity to Poole, Dorchester and the Purbeck coast. Two luxury blocks, with combined washbasin/WCs for total privacy, maintain a high standard of cleanliness. A heated outdoor swimming pool, off licence, shop and games room add to the pleasure of a stay here. A 55 acre site with 200 touring pitches, 70 hardstandings.

Leisure:

Facilities:

Services:

Within 3 miles:

Notes: Families & couples only, no group bookings. Wi-fi

WAREHAM

►►► 84% Birchwood Tourist Park

Bere Rd, Coldharbour BH20 7PA

☎ 01929 554763 01929 556635

dir: *From Poole (A351) or Dorchester (A352) on N side of railway line at Wareham, follow road signed Bere Regis (unclassified). 2nd tourist park after 2.25m*

Open 13 Dec-23 Nov Last arrival 21.00hrs Last departure 11.30hrs

Set in 50 acres of parkland located within Wareham Forest, this site offers direct access into ideal areas for walking, mountain biking, and horse and pony riding. The modern facilities are centrally located and well-organised. A 25 acre site with 175 touring pitches, 25 hardstandings.

Leisure:

Facilities:

Services:

Within 3 miles:

Notes: No generators, no groups on Bank Holidays, no camp fires. Games field, bike hire, pitch & putt, paddling pool

WAREHAM

►►► 79% Lookout Holiday Park

Stoborough BH20 5AZ

☎ 01929 552546 01929 556662

e-mail: enquiries@caravan-sites.co.uk

web: www.caravan-sites.co.uk

dir: *Take A351 through Wareham, after crossing River Frome & through Stoborough, site signed on left*

* £15-£28 £15-£28 £12-£24

Open all year Last arrival 22.00hrs Last departure noon

Divided into two paddocks and set well back from the Swanage road, this touring park is separated from the static part of the operation. A superb children's playground and plenty of other attractions make this an ideal centre for families. A 15 acre site with 150 touring pitches, 94 hardstandings and 89 statics.

Leisure:

Facilities:

Services:

Within 3 miles:

Notes: Family park. No pets. Wi-fi

WAREHAM

►►► 77%

East Creech Farm Campsite

East Creech Farm, East Creech BH20 5AP

☎ 01929 480519 & 481312

01929 480519

e-mail: east.creech@virgin.net

dir: *From Wareham on A351 S towards Swanage. On bypass at 3rd rdbt take Furzebrook/Blue Pool Rd exit, approx 2m site on right*

Open Apr-Oct

A grassy park set in a peaceful location beneath the Purbeck Hills, with extensive views towards Poole and Brownsea Island. The park boasts a woodland play area, bright, clean toilet facilities, and a farm shop selling milk, eggs and bread. There are also three coarse fishing lakes teeming with fish. The park is close to the Norden Station on the Swanage to Norden steam railway, and is well located for visting Corfe Castle, Swanage and the Purbeck coast. A 4 acre site with 80 touring pitches.

Leisure: **Facilities:**
Services: **Within 3 miles:**
Notes:

WEYMOUTH

83% Littlesea Holiday Park

Lynch Ln DT4 9DT

☎ 01305 774414 01305 759186

dir: *A35 onto A354 signed Weymouth. Right at 1st rdbt, 3rd exit at 2nd rdbt towards Chickerell. Left into Lynch Lane after lights. Site at far end of road*

* £11-£100 £11-£100 £11-£66

Open end Mar-end Oct (rs mid Mar-May & Sep-Oct facilities may be reduced) Last arrival mdnt Last departure 10.00hrs

Just three miles from Weymouth with its lovely beaches and many attractions, Littlesea has a cheerful family atmosphere and fantastic facilities. Indoor and outdoor entertainment and activities are on offer for all the family, and the toilet facilities on the touring park are of a good quality. A 100 acre site with 124 touring pitches and 720 statics.

Leisure:
Facilities:
Services:
Within 3 miles:
Notes: No commercial vehicles, no boats, no dangerous dog breeds. Wi-fi

WEYMOUTH

75% Seaview Holiday Park

Preston DT3 6DZ

01305 833037 01305 833169

e-mail: katie.watson@bourne-leisure.co.uk

dir: *A354 to Weymouth, signs for Preston/ Wareham onto A353. Site 3m on right just after Weymouth Bay Holiday Park*

* £9-£79 £9-£79 £9-£52

Open mid Mar-Oct (rs Mid Mar-May & Sep-Oct facilities may be reduced) Last arrival mdnt Last departure noon

A fun-packed holiday centre for all the family, with plenty of activities and entertainment during the day and evening. Terraced pitches are provided for caravans, and there is a separate field for tents. The park is close to Weymouth and other coastal attractions. Seasonal touring pitches are available. A 20 acre site with 87 touring pitches, 24 hardstandings and 259 statics.

Leisure:

Facilities:

Services:

Within 3 miles:

Notes: No groups bookings under 21yrs, noise to be kept at minimum outside complex, certain dog breeds banned. Wi-fi

WEYMOUTH

►►►► 92% East Fleet Farm Touring Park

Chickerell DT3 4DW

01305 785768

e-mail: enquiries@eastfleet.co.uk

dir: *On B3157 (Weymouth-Bridport road), 3m from Weymouth*

* £10.75-£19.50 £10.75-£19.50 £10.75-£19.50

Open 16 Mar-Oct Last arrival 22.00hrs Last departure 10.30hrs

Set on a working organic farm overlooking Fleet Lagoon and Chesil Beach, with a wide range of amenities and quality toilet facilities in a Scandinavian log cabin. The friendly owners are welcoming and helpful, and their family bar serving meals and takeaway food is open from Easter, with glorious views from the patio area. A 21 acre site with 400 touring pitches, 50 hardstandings.

Leisure:

Facilities:

Services:

Within 3 miles:

Notes: Large camping accessories shop

WEYMOUTH

►►►►

77% Bagwell Farm Touring Park

Knights in the Bottom, Chickerell DT3 4EA

☎ 01305 782575 01305 780554

e-mail: aa@bagwellfarm.co.uk

web: www.bagwellfarm.co.uk

dir: *4m W of Weymouth on B3157 (Weymouth-Bridport), past Chickerell, turn left into site 500yds after Victoria Inn*

Open all year (rs Winter bar closed) Last arrival 21.00hrs Last departure 11.00hrs

An idyllically-placed terraced site on a hillside and a valley overlooking Chesil Beach. The park is well equipped with 25 new fully-serviced pitches, mini-supermarket, children's play area and pets corner, and a bar and grill serving food in high season. A 14 acre site with 320 touring pitches, 10 hardstandings.

Leisure:

Facilities:

Services:

Within 3 miles:

Notes: Families only. Dogs must be kept on leads. Wet suit shower, campers' shelter

WEYMOUTH

►►►

78% West Fleet Holiday Farm

Fleet DT3 4EF

☎ 01305 782218 01305 775396

e-mail: aa@westfleetholidays.co.uk

web: www.westfleetholidays.co.uk

dir: *From Weymouth take B3157 towards Abbotsbury for 3m. Past Chickerell turn left at mini-rdbt to Fleet, site 1m on right*

£12-£24 £12-£24

Open Etr-Sep (rs May-Sep pool available) Last arrival 22.00hrs Last departure 11.00hrs

A spacious farm site with both level and sloping pitches divided into paddocks, and screened with hedging. Good views of the Dorset countryside, and a relaxing site for a family holiday with its heated outdoor pool and club house. A 12 acre site with 250 touring pitches.

Leisure:

Facilities:

Services:

Within 3 miles:

Notes: Non-family groups by arrangement only, dogs must be on leads at all times & restricted to certain areas. Games field

WIMBORNE MINSTER

►►►►► 83% Wilksworth Farm Caravan Park

Cranborne Rd BH21 4HW

☎ 01202 885467 📠 01202 885467

e-mail: rayandwendy@wilksworthfarmcaravanpark.co.uk

web: www.wilksworthfarmcaravanpark.co.uk

dir: *1m N of Wimborne on B3078*

Open Apr-Oct (rs Apr & Oct no shop or coffee shop) Last arrival 20.00hrs Last departure 11.00hrs

A popular and attractive park set in the grounds of a listed house, located in the heart of rural Dorset. The spacious site has much to offer visitors, including a heated swimming pool, takeaway and café, and games room. The ultra-modern toilet facilities contain en suite rooms. An11 acre site with 85 touring pitches, 20 hardstandings and 77 statics.

Leisure:

Facilities:

Services:

Within 3 miles:

Notes: Paddling pool, volley ball, mini football pitch

WIMBORNE MINSTER

►►►►► 74% Merley Court

Merley BH21 3AA

☎ 01590 648331 📠 01590 645610

e-mail: holidays@shorefield.co.uk

dir: *Site signed on A31, Wimborne by-pass & Poole junct rdbt*

Open 6 Feb-2 Jan (rs Low season pool closed & bar, shop open limited hrs) Last arrival 21.00hrs Last departure 10.00hrs

A superb site in a quiet rural position on the edge of Wimborne, with woodland on two sides and good access roads. The park is well landscaped, and offers generous individual pitches in sheltered grassland. There are plenty of amenities for all the family, including heated outdoor pool, tennis court and adventure playground. A 20 acre site with 160 touring pitches, 50 hardstandings.

Leisure:

Facilities:

Services:

Within 3 miles:

Notes: Families & couples only. Pet friendly. Rallies welcome. Use of facilities at Oakdene Forest Park (7m)

WOOL

►►►► 80%

Whitemead Caravan Park

East Burton Rd BH20 6HG

☎ 01929 462241 📠 01929 462241

e-mail: whitemeadcp@aol.com

dir: *Signed from A352 at level crossing on Wareham side of Wool*

* £11.75-£18.50 £11.75-£18.50 £9.50-£16.25

Open mid Mar-Oct Last arrival 22.00hrs Last departure noon

A well laid-out site in the valley of the River Frome, close to the village and surrounded by woodland. A shop and games room enhance the facilities here, and the toilets are heated, providing an excellent amenity. A short walk away are the local shops and pubs, and the main bus route and mainline station to Poole, Bournemouth and Weymouth. Other nearby attractions include Bovington Tank Museum and Monkey World. A 5 acre site with 95 touring pitches.

Leisure:

Facilities:

Services:

Within 3 miles:

Notes: Wi-fi

BEAMISH

►►► 74%

Bobby Shafto Caravan Park

Cranberry Plantation DH9 0RY

☎ 0191 370 1776 📠 0191 370 1783

dir: *From A693 signed Beamish to sign for Beamish Museum. Take approach road, turn right immediately before museum, left at pub to site 1m on right*

Open Mar-Oct Last arrival 23.00hrs Last departure 11.00hrs

A tranquil rural park surrounded by trees, with very clean and well-organised facilities. The suntrap touring area has plenty of attractive hanging baskets, and there is a clubhouse with bar, TV and pool. The fully serviced pitches enhance the amenities. A 9 acre site with 83 touring pitches, 30 hardstandings and 54 statics.

Leisure:

Facilities:

Services:

Within 3 miles:

BLACKHALL COLLIERY

79% Crimdon Dene

Coast Rd TS27 4BN

☎ 0871 664 9737

e-mail: crimdon.dene@park-resorts.com

dir: *From A19 just S of Peterlee, take B1281 signed Blackhall. Through Castle Eden, left in 0.5m signed Blackhall. Approx 3m right at T-junct onto A1086 towards Crimdon. Site in 1m signed on left, by Seagull pub*

* £7-£28 £7-£28

Open Mar-Oct Last arrival 23.00hrs Last departure 10.00hrs

A large, popular coastal holiday park, handily placed for access to Teeside, Durham and Newcastle. The park contains a full range of holiday centre facilities for both children and their parents. Touring facilities are to a very good standard. 43 touring pitches and 586 statics.

Leisure:
Facilities:
Services:
Within 3 miles:
Notes: No quad bikes

CLACTON-ON-SEA

78% Highfield Grange

London Rd CO16 9QY

☎ 0871 664 9746 01255 689805

e-mail: highfield.grange@park-resorts.com

dir: *A12 to Colchester, then A120 (Harwich) then A133 to Clacton-on-Sea. Site on B1441 clearly signed on left*

Open 31 Mar-Oct Last departure noon

The modern leisure facilities at this attractively planned park make it an ideal base for a lively family holiday. The swimming complex with both indoor and outdoor pools and a huge water shoot is especially popular. There are fully serviced touring pitches, each with its own hard standing, located at the heart of the park. The nearby resorts of Walton on the Naze, Frinton and Clacton all offer excellent beaches and a wide range of popular seaside attractions. 43 touring pitches, 43 hardstandings and 509 statics.

Leisure:
Facilities:
Services:
Within 3 miles:
Notes: No tents, fold-in campers or trailer tents

CLACTON-ON-SEA

70% Martello Beach Holiday Park

Belsize Av, Jaywick CO15 2LF

☎ 0871 664 9782 & 01442 830100

e-mail: martello.beach@park-resorts.com

dir: *Telephone for directions*

Open Mar-Oct (rs BH & peak wks Entertainment available) Last arrival 20.00hrs Last departure 10.00hrs

Direct access to a 7-mile long Blue Flag beach is an undoubted attraction at this holiday park. The touring area is next to the leisure complex, where an indoor and outdoor swimming pool, shops, cafés, bars and evening entertainment are all provided. A 40 acre site with 150 touring pitches and 294 statics.

Leisure:
Facilities:
Services:
Within 3 miles:
Notes: Kids' clubs, water sports

MERSEA ISLAND

77% Waldegraves Holiday Park

CO5 8SE

☎ 01206 382898 01206 385359

e-mail: holidays@waldegraves.co.uk

web: www.waldegraves.co.uk

dir: *B1025 to Mersea Island across The Strood. Left to East Mersea, 2nd turn on right, follow tourist signs to site*

£12-£25 £12-£25 £12-£25

Open Mar-Nov Last arrival 22.00hrs Last departure noon

A spacious and pleasant site, located between farmland and its own private beach on the Blackwater Estuary. Facilities include two freshwater fishing lakes, heated swimming pool, club, amusements, café and golf, and there is generally good provision for families. A 25 acre site with 60 touring pitches and 250 statics.

Leisure:
Facilities:
Services:
Within 3 miles:
Notes: No large groups or groups of under 21s. Boating. Wi-fi

ST LAWRENCE

79% Waterside St Lawrence Bay

Main Rd CM0 7LY

☎ 0871 664 9794

e-mail: waterside@park-resorts.com

dir: *A12 towards Chelmsford then A414 signed Maldon. Follow B1010 & signs to Latchingdon, then signs for Mayland/Steeple/ St Lawrence. Left towards St Lawrence. Site on right*

Open Mar-Oct (rs wknds Entertainment available) Last arrival 19.00hrs Last departure 10.00hrs

Waterside occupies a scenic location overlooking the Blackwater estuary. In addition to the range of onsite leisure facilities there are opportunities for coastal walks and visits to Southend. Tents are welcome on this expansive site; 70 of the touring pitches have electricity, and there are good toilet facilities. The park has its own boat storage and slipway onto the Blackwater. 100 touring pitches and 211 statics.

Leisure: **Facilities:** **Services:** **Within 3 miles:**

ST OSYTH

The Orchards Holiday Park

CO16 8LJ

☎ 01255 820651 01255 820184

e-mail: laura.hassall@bourne-leisure.co.uk

dir: *From Clacton-on-Sea take B1027 towards Colchester. Left after petrol station, then straight on at x-rds in St Osyth. Follow signs to Point Clear. Park in 3m*

Open end Mar-end Oct (rs mid Mar-May & Sep-Oct some facilities may be reduced) Last arrival anytime Last departure 10.00hrs

The newly created touring area is conveniently located to all the leisure attractions, shops, cafés and bars at this popular holiday park on the Essex coast. At the time of going to press the rating for this site had not been confirmed. For up-to-date information please see the AA website: theAA.com. A 140 acre site with 30 touring pitches and 1000 statics.

Leisure:

Facilities:

Services:

Within 3 miles:

Notes: No cars by tents Certain dog breeds banned. Wi-fi

WALTON ON THE NAZE

73% Naze Marine

Hall Ln CO14 8HL

☎ 0871 664 9755

e-mail: naze.marine@park-resorts.com

dir: *A12 to Colchester. Then A120 (Harwich road) then A133 to Weeley. Take B1033 to Walton seafront. Site on left*

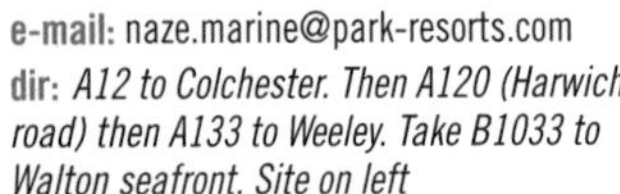

Open Mar-Oct

With its modern indoor swimming pool, show bar, bar/restaurant and amusements, this park offers a variety of on-site attractions. The park is within easy access of the beaches and attractions of Walton on the Naze, Frinton and Clacton, and the more historic places of interest inland. This site does not cater for tents. 41 touring pitches and 540 statics.

Leisure:
Facilities:
Services:
Within 3 miles:

BERKELEY

►►► 74% Hogsdown Farm Caravan & Camping Park

Hogsdown Farm, Lower Wick GL11 6DD

☎ 01453 810224

dir: *M5 junct 14 (Falfield), take A38 towards Gloucester, turn right for site*

Open all year Last arrival 21.00hrs Last departure 16.00hrs

A pleasant site with good toilet facilities, located between Bristol and Gloucester. It is well positioned for visiting Berkeley Castle and the Cotswold Edge country, and makes an excellent overnight stop when travelling to or from the West Country. A 5 acre site with 45 touring pitches, 12 hardstandings.

Leisure:
Facilities:
Services:
Within 3 miles:
Notes: No skateboards or bicycles

WINCHCOMBE

►►► 83% Winchcombe Camping & Caravanning Club Site

Brooklands Farm, Alderton GL20 8NX

☎ 01242 620259

dir: *M5 junct 9 onto A46, straight on at rdbt onto B4077 signed Stow-on-the-Wold. Site 3m on right*

Open 16 Mar-15 Jan Last arrival 21.00hrs Last departure noon

A pleasant rural park with pitches spaced around two attractive lakes offering good fishing, and the benefit of a long season. This flower-filled park is in an area of historic buildings and picturesque villages between Cheltenham and Tewkesbury. A 20 acre site with 80 touring pitches, 63 hardstandings.

Leisure:

Facilities:

Services:

Within 3 miles:

Notes: Site gates closed 23.00hrs-07.00hrs. Pool table, table tennis

CRAWLEY

►►► 70% Folly Farm Touring Caravan Park

Crawley SO21 2PH

☎ 01962 776486

dir: *Midway between Winchester & Stockbridge on B3049. Site 0.75m past Rack & Manger pub*

* fr £16 fr £16 £12-£16

Open all year Last arrival 22.00hrs

A small farm site set in rural mid-Hampshire between Stockbridge and Winchester, ideal for visiting the ancient capital of Wessex or the New Forest, and the south coast is only a short drive away. The clean facilities are located in farm outbuildings, and there is a small campers' kitchen. A 2.5 acre site with 30 touring pitches, 3 hardstandings.

Leisure:

Facilities:

Services:

Within 3 miles:

Notes: No children in farm area. Dogs must be kept on leads. Local info & local produce available

FORDINGBRIDGE

90% Sandy Balls Holiday Centre

Sandy Balls Estate Ltd, Godshill SP6 2JZ

☎ 0845 270 2248 🖷 01425 653067

e-mail: post@sandy-balls.co.uk

web: www.sandy-balls.co.uk

dir: *M27 junct 1 onto B3078/B3079, W 8m to Godshill. Site 0.25m after cattle grid*

Open all year (rs Nov-Feb pitches reduced, no activities) Last arrival 21.00hrs Last departure 11.00hrs

A large New Forest holiday complex with good provision of touring facilities on terraced, well laid-out fields. Pitches are fully serviced with shingle bases, and groups can be sited by the river, away from the main site. Excellent sport, leisure and entertainment facilities for the whole family, a new bistro and information centre. 4 tipis and 8 ready-erected tents for hire. A 120 acre site with 233 touring pitches, 233 hardstandings and 233 statics.

Leisure: **Facilities:** **Services:** **Within 3 miles:**

Notes: Groups by arrangement only. No gazebos. Jacuzzi, sauna, gym, horse riding

MILFORD ON SEA

►►► 86% Lytton Lawn Touring Park

Lymore Ln SO41 0TX

☎ 01590 648331 🖷 01590 645610

e-mail: holidays@shorefield.co.uk

dir: *From Lymington A337 to Christchurch for 2.5m to Everton. Left onto B3058 to Milford on Sea. 0.25m, left onto Lymore Lane*

Open 6 Feb-2 Jan (rs Low season shop/reception ltd hrs. No grass pitches) Last arrival 22.00hrs Last departure 10.00hrs

A pleasant well-run park with good facilities, near the coast. The park is peaceful and quiet, but the facilities of a sister park 2.5 miles away are available to campers, including swimming pool, tennis courts, bistro and bar/carvery, and large club with family entertainment. Fully-serviced pitches provide good screening, and standard pitches are on gently-sloping grass. An 8 acre site with 136 touring pitches, 53 hardstandings.

Leisure: **Facilities:** **Services:** **Within 3 miles:** **Notes:** Families & couples only. Pet friendly. Rallies welcome. Free use of Shorefield Leisure Club (2.5m)

ROMSEY

►►►► 88%

Hill Farm Caravan Park

Branches Ln, Sherfield English SO51 6FH

☎ 01794 340402 01794 342358

e-mail: gjb@hillfarmpark.com

dir: *Signed from A27 (Salisbury to Romsey road) in Sherfield English, 4m NW of Romsey & M27 junct 2*

Open Mar-Oct Last arrival 20.00hrs Last departure noon

A small, well-sheltered park peacefully located amidst mature trees and meadows. The two toilet blocks offer smart unisex showers as well as a fully en suite family/disabled room and plenty of privacy in the wash rooms. The owners continue to develop this attractive park, and with its proximity to Salisbury and the New Forest, it makes an appealing holiday location. A 10.5 acre site with 70 touring pitches, 60 hardstandings and 6 statics.

Leisure: **Facilities:** **Services:** **Within 3 miles:** **Notes:** Minimum noise at all times & no noise after 23.00hrs. One unit per pitch 9-hole pitch & putt, badminton. Wi-fi

PEMBRIDGE

►►►►► 84%

Townsend Touring Park

Townsend Farm HR6 9HB

☎ 01544 388527

e-mail: info@townsend-farm.co.uk

dir: *A44 through Pembridge. Site 40mtrs from 30mph on E side of village*

* £11-£21 £11-£21 £11-£21

Open Mar-mid Jan Last arrival 22.00hrs Last departure noon

This outstanding park is spaciously located on the edge of one of Herefordshire's most beautiful Black and White villages. The park offers excellent facilities, and all hardstanding pitches are fully serviced, and has its own award-winning farm shop and butchery. It also makes an excellent base from which to explore the local area including Ludlow Castle and Ironbridge. 8 seasonal touring pitches available. A 12 acre site with 60 touring pitches, 23 hardstandings.

Leisure:

Facilities:

Services:

Within 3 miles:

SYMONDS YAT (WEST)

►►► 81% Doward Park Camp Site

Great Doward HR9 6BP

☎ 01600 890438

e-mail: enquiries@dowardpark.co.uk

dir: *2m from A40 between Ross-on-Wye & Monmouth. Take Symonds Yat (West) turn, then Crockers Ash, follow signs to site*

Open Mar-Oct Last arrival 20.00hrs Last departure 11.30hrs

This delightful little park is set in peaceful woodlands on the hillside above the Wye Valley. It is ideal for campers and motor homes but not caravans due to the narrow approach roads. A warm welcome awaits and the facilities are kept spotless. 5 seasonal touring pitches available. A 1.5 acre site with 28 touring pitches.

Leisure:

Facilities:

Services:

Within 3 miles:

Notes: No caravans or fires, quiet after 22.00hrs, dogs must be kept on leads

HERTFORD

►►►► 77% Hertford Camping & Caravanning Club Site

Mangrove Rd SG13 8QF

☎ 01992 586696

dir: *From A10 follow A414/Hertford signs to next rdbt (Foxholes), straight over. In 200yds left signed Balls Park & Hertford University. Left at T-junct into Mangrove Road. Site on left*

Open all year Last arrival 21.00hrs Last departure noon

A spacious, well-landscaped club site in a rural setting one mile south of Hertford, with immaculate modern toilet facilities. There are several hedged areas with good provision of hardstandings, and a cosy camping section in an old orchard. All kinds of wildlife flourish around the lake. A 32 acre site with 250 touring pitches, 54 hardstandings.

Leisure:

Facilities:

Services:

Within 3 miles:

Notes: Site gates closed 23.00hrs-07.00hrs

WALTHAM CROSS

►►► 74% Theobalds Park Camping & Caravanning Club Site

Theobalds Park, Bulls Cross Ride EN7 5HS

☎ 01992 620604

dir: *M25 junct 25. A10 towards London keep in right lane. Right at 1st lights. Right at T-junct, right behind dog kennels. Site towards top of lane on right*

Open 2 Apr-2 Nov Last arrival 21.00hrs Last departure noon

A lovely open site surrounded by mature trees, and set in parkland at Theobalds Hall. New portacabin toilets have improved the facilities, and there are two separate glades for tents. A 14 acre site with 90 touring pitches.

Leisure:

Facilities:

Services:

Within 3 miles:

Notes: Site gates closed 23.00hrs-07.00hrs

ASHFORD

►►►► 87% Broad Hembury Caravan & Camping Park

Steeds Ln, Kingsnorth TN26 1NQ

☎ 01233 620859 01233 620918

e-mail: holidaypark@broadhembury.co.uk

web: www.broadhembury.co.uk

dir: *From M20 junct 10 take A2070. Left at 2nd rdbt signed Kingsnorth, then left at 2nd x-roads in village*

Open all year Last arrival 22.00hrs Last departure noon

Well-run and maintained small family park surrounded by open pasture and neatly landscaped, with pitches sheltered by mature hedges. Some super pitches have proved a popular addition, and there is a well-equipped campers' kitchen. A 10 acre site with 60 touring pitches, 24 hardstandings and 25 statics.

Leisure:

Facilities:

Services:

Within 3 miles:

Notes: Sports field. Wi-fi

BIRCHINGTON

►►► 79% Two Chimneys Caravan Park

Shottendane Rd CT7 0HD

☎ 01843 841068 & 843157

01843 848099

e-mail: info@twochimneys.co.uk

dir: *From A28 to Birchington Sq, right into Park Lane (B2048). Left at Manston Road (B2050) then 1st left*

* £14-£26.50 £14-£26.50 £14-£26.50

Open Mar-Oct (rs Mar-May & Sep-Oct shop, bar, pool & takeaway restricted) Last arrival 22.00hrs Last departure noon

An impressive entrance leads into this well-managed site, which has two swimming pools and a fully-licensed clubhouse. Other attractions include a tennis court and children's play area. The immaculately clean toilet facilities fully meet the needs of this busy family park. 15 seasonal touring pitches available. A 40 acre site with 200 touring pitches, 5 hardstandings and 200 statics.

Leisure: **Facilities:** **Services:** **Within 3 miles:** **Notes:** Amusement arcade

CANTERBURY

►►► 85% Canterbury Camping & Caravanning Club Site

Bekesbourne Ln CT3 4AB

☎ 01227 463216

dir: *From Canterbury follow A257 signs (Sandwich), turn right opposite golf course*

Open all year Last arrival 21.00hrs Last departure noon

An attractive tree-screened site in pleasant rural surroundings yet within walking distance of the city centre. The park is well landscaped, and offers very smart toilet facilities in one block, with another older but well-kept building housing further facilities. A 20 acre site with 200 touring pitches, 21 hardstandings.

Leisure:

Facilities:

Services:

Within 3 miles:

EASTCHURCH

74% Warden Springs Caravan Park

Warden Point ME12 4HF

☎ 01795 880216 01795 880218

dir: *From M2 junct 5 (Sheerness/ Sittingbourne) follow A249 for 8m, right onto B2231 to Eastchurch. In Eastchurch left after church follow park signs*

Open Mar-Oct (rs BH & peak wks entertainment available) Last arrival 19.00hrs Last departure 10.00hrs

Panoramic views from the scenic clifftop setting can be enjoyed at their best from the touring area of this holiday park. All of the many and varied leisure activities provided by the park are included in the pitch tariff, including a heated outdoor swimming pool, an adventure playground, family entertainment and a good choice of food outlets. 48 touring pitches and 198 statics.

Leisure:

Facilities:

Services:

Within 3 miles:

Notes: No cars by caravans or tents

LEYSDOWN-ON-SEA

►►► 71% Priory Hill

Wing Rd ME12 4QT

☎ 01795 510267 01795 511503

e-mail: touringpark@prioryhill.co.uk

dir: *Take A249 signed Sheerness then B2231 to Leysdown, follow brown tourist signs*

* £13-£25 £13-£23 £13-£23

Open Mar-Oct (rs Low season shorter opening times of pool & club) Last arrival 20.00hrs Last departure noon

A small well-maintained touring area on an established family-run holiday park close to the sea, with views of the North Kent coast. Amenities include a clubhouse and a swimming pool. The pitch price includes membership of clubhouse with live entertainment, and use of indoor swimming pool. A 1.5 acre site with 37 touring pitches.

Leisure:

Facilities:

Services:

Within 3 miles:

Notes: Wi-fi

SEVENOAKS

►►► 72% Oldbury Hill Camping & Caravanning Club Site

Styants Bottom, Seal TN15 0ET

☎ 01732 762728

dir: *Take A25 from Sevenoaks towards Borough Green. Left just after Crown Point Inn, on right, down narrow lane to Styants Bottom. Site on left*

Open 2 Apr-2 Nov Last arrival 21.00hrs Last departure noon

A remarkably tranquil site in the centre of National Trust woodland, with buildings blending well into the surroundings. Expect the usual high standard of customer care found at all Club sites. A 6 acre site with 60 touring pitches.

Leisure:

Facilities:

Services:

Within 3 miles:

Notes: Site gates closed 23.00hrs-07.00hrs

WHITSTABLE

►►►► 82% Homing Park

Church Ln, Seasalter CT5 4BU

☎ 01227 771777 01227 273512

e-mail: info@homingpark.co.uk

dir: *Exit A299 for Whitstable & Canterbury, left at brown camping-caravan sign into Church Ln. Site entrance has 2 large flag poles*

* £17-£22 £17-£22 £17-£22

Open Etr-Oct Last arrival 20.00hrs Last departure 11.00hrs

A small touring park close to Seasalter Beach and Whitstable, which is famous for its oysters. All pitches are generously sized and fully serviced, and most are separated by hedging and shrubs. A clubhouse and swimming pool are available on the adjacent residential park at a small cost. A 12.6 acre site with 43 touring pitches and 195 statics.

Leisure:

Facilities:

Services:

Within 3 miles:

Notes: No commercial vehicles, no tents greater than 8 berth or 5mtrs, no unaccompanied minors. Wi-fi

WHITSTABLE

►►► 75% Seaview Holiday Village

St John's Rd CT5 2RY

☎ 01227 792246 Fax 01227 792247

e-mail: info@parkholidaysuk.com

dir: *From A299 take A2990 then B2205 to Swalecliffe, site between Herne Bay & Whitstable*

Open Mar-Oct Last arrival 21.30hrs Last departure noon

A pleasant open site on the edge of Whitstable, set well away from the static area, with a smart, modern toilet block and both super and hardstanding pitches. A 12 acre site with 171 touring pitches, 41 hardstandings and 452 statics.

Leisure:

Facilities:

Services:

Within 3 miles:

Notes: Amusements in games room & adventure trail

WROTHAM HEATH

►►► 76% Gate House Wood Touring Park

Ford Ln TN15 7SD

☎ 01732 843062

e-mail: gatehousewood@btinternet.com

dir: *M26 junct 2a, A20 S towards Maidstone, through lights at Wrotham Heath. 1st left signed Trottiscliffe, left at next junct into Ford Ln. Site 100yds on left*

Open Mar-Oct Last arrival 22.00hrs Last departure noon

A well-sheltered and mature site in a former quarry surrounded by tall deciduous trees and gorse banks. The well-designed facilities include reception, shop and smart toilets, and there is good entrance security. Conveniently placed for the M20 and M25. A 3.5 acre site with 55 touring pitches.

Leisure:

Facilities:

Services:

Within 3 miles:

Notes: No commercial vehicles, no pets

BLACKPOOL

77% Marton Mere Holiday Village

Mythop Rd FY4 4XN

01253 767544 01253 791252

dir: *M55 junct 4, A583 towards Blackpool. Right at Clifton Arms lights, onto Mythop Rd. Site 150yds on left*

* £12-£80 £12-£80

Open mid Mar-Oct (rs Mar-end May & Sep-Oct reduced facilities, splash zone closed) Last arrival anytime Last departure 10.00hrs

A very attractive holiday centre on the edge of the mere, with plenty of birdlife. The on-site entertainment is directed at all ages, and includes a superb show bar. There's a regular bus service into Blackpool for those who want to explore further afield. The separate touring area is well equipped with hardstandings and electric pitches, and there are good quality facilities. 25 seasonal touring pitches available. A 30 acre site with 197 touring pitches, 197 hardstandings and 700 statics.

Leisure: **Facilities:** **Services:** **Within 3 miles:** **Notes:** No more than 2 dogs per group, certain dog breeds banned, no adult-only groups

BOLTON-LE-SANDS

►►► 82% Bay View Holiday Park

LA5 9TN

01524 733617 01524 730612

e-mail: info@holgateleisureparks.co.uk

dir: *W of A6, 1m N of Bolton-le-Sands*

* £10-£20 £10-£20 £10-£20

Open Mar-Oct (rs Mar-May shop hours restricted) Last arrival 22.00hrs Last departure 18.00hrs

This very attractive, very extensive park overlooks Morecombe Bay, and has the advantage of sloping in such a way that nearly every pitch has a spectacular view of the Bay and the Cumbrian Hills beyond. It is an amalgamation of two parks, and offers superior facilities and amenities for all the family. 14 seasonal touring pitches available. A 10 acre site with 100 touring pitches, 100 hardstandings and 42 statics.

Leisure:

Facilities:

Services:

Within 3 miles:

GARSTANG

►►►► 81% Claylands Caravan Park

Cabus PR3 1AJ

☎ 01524 791242 📠 01524 792406

e-mail: alan@claylands.com

dir: *From M6 junct 33 S to Garstang, approx 6m pass Quttros Restaurant, signed off A6 into private road on Lancaster side of Garstang*

£13-£15 £13-£15 ▲ £13-£15

Open Mar-4 Jan Last arrival 23.00hrs Last departure noon

A well-maintained site with lovely river and woodland walks and good views over the River Wyre towards the village of Scorton. Guests can enjoy fishing, and the atmosphere is very relaxed. The quality facilities and amenities are of a high standard, and everything is immaculately maintained. A 14 acre site with 30 touring pitches, 30 hardstandings and 68 statics.

Leisure:

Facilities:

Services:

Within 3 miles:

Notes: Pets must be kept on leads, no roller blades or skateboards

MORECAMBE

►►► 78% Venture Caravan Park

Langridge Way, Westgate LA4 4TQ

☎ 01524 412986 📠 01524 422029

e-mail: mark@venturecaravanpark.co.uk

dir: *From M6 junct 34 follow Morecambe signs. At rdbt take road towards Westgate & follow site signs. 1st right after fire station*

* fr £18 fr £18 ▲ fr £15

Open end Feb-Dec (rs 6 Jan-22 Feb touring vans only, one toilet block open) Last arrival 22.00hrs Last departure noon

A large park with good modern facilities, including a small indoor heated pool, a licensed clubhouse and a family room with children's entertainment. The site has many statics, and is close to the town centre. A 17.5 acre site with 56 touring pitches, 40 hardstandings and 304 statics.

Leisure:

Facilities:

Services:

Within 3 miles:

Notes: Amusement arcade, off licence

ORMSKIRK

►►►► 79%

Abbey Farm Caravan Park

Dark Ln L40 5TX

☎ 01695 572686 01695 572686

e-mail: abbeyfarm@yahoo.com

dir: *M6 junct 27 onto A5209 to Burscough. 4m left onto B5240. Immediate right into Hobcross Ln. Site 1.5m on right*

Open all year Last arrival 21.00hrs Last departure noon

Delightful hanging baskets and flower beds brighten this garden-like rural park which is sheltered by hedging and mature trees. Modern, very clean facilities include a family bathroom, and there are special pitches for the disabled near the toilets. A superb recreation field caters for children of all ages, and there is an indoor games room, large library, fishing lake and dog walk. Tents have their own area with BBQ and picnic tables. A 6 acre site with 56 touring pitches and 44 statics.

Leisure: **Facilities:** **Services:**
Within 3 miles:
Notes: No camp fires. Off-licence, farm walk

SILVERDALE

►►►►► 95%

Holgate's Caravan Park

Middlebarrow Plain, Cove Rd LA5 0SH

☎ 01524 701508 01524 701580

e-mail: caravan@holgates.co.uk

dir: *M6 junct 35. 5m NW of Carnforth. From Carnforth centre take unclass Silverdale road & follow tourist signs after Warton*

* £32.50-£33.50 £32.50-£33.50 £29.50-£33.50

Open 22 Dec-7 Nov Last arrival 20.00hrs Last departure noon

A superb family holiday park set in wooded countryside next to the sea. This park demonstrates high quality in all areas, and offers a wide range of leisure amenities. Its relaxing position overlooking Morecambe Bay combined with excellent touring facilities mark this park out as special. 2 seasonal touring pitches available. A 10 acre site with 80 touring pitches, 80 hardstandings and 339 statics.

Leisure: **Facilities:** **Services:**
Within 3 miles:
Notes: No unaccompanied children. Sauna, spa bath, steam room, mini-golf, gym. Wi-fi

THORNTON

►►►► 79% Kneps Farm Holiday Park

River Rd, Stanah FY5 5LR

☎ 01253 823632 01253 863967

e-mail: enquiries@knepsfarm.co.uk

web: www.knepsfarm.co.uk

dir: *Exit A585 at rdbt onto B5412 to Little Thornton. Right at mini-rdbt after school onto Stanah Rd, over 2nd mini-rdbt, leading to River Rd*

* £17.50-£19 £17.50-£19 £14.50-£19

Open Mar-mid Nov (rs Apr-early Nov shop open) Last arrival 20.00hrs Last dep noon

Next to the River Wyre and the Wyre Estuary, handy for Blackpool and the Fylde coast, Kneps Farm offers an excellent toilet block, immaculate facilities, and a mixture of hard and grass pitches. Although quietly located, there may be some noise from a nearby plastics plant. 10 acre site with 60 touring pitches, 40 hardstandings and 60 statics.

Leisure: **Facilities:** **Services:** **Within 3 miles:** **Notes:** No commercial vehicles. Max 2 dogs per group, dogs must be kept on leads & are chargeable

ANCASTER

►►► 80% Woodland Waters

Willoughby Rd NG32 3RT

☎ 01400 230888 01400 230888

e-mail: info@woodlandwaters.co.uk

web: www.woodlandwaters.co.uk

dir: *On A153 W of x-roads with B6403*

* £14-£17 £14-£17 £14-£17

Open all year Last arrival 21.00hrs Last departure noon

Peacefully set around five impressive fishing lakes, with a few log cabins in a separate area, this is a pleasant open park. The access road is through mature woodland, and there is an excellent new heated toilet block, and a pub/club house with restaurant. A 72 acre site with 62 touring pitches, 2 hardstandings.

Leisure:

Facilities:

Services:

Within 3 miles:

Notes: Dogs must be kept on leads at all times

BOSTON

►►►► 78% Pilgrims Way Caravan & Camping Park

Church Green Rd, Fishtoft PE21 0QY

☎ 01205 366646 📠 01205 366646

e-mail: pilgrimsway@caravanandcampingpark.com

dir: *E from Boston on A52. In 1m, after junct with A16, at Ball House pub turn right. Follow tourist signs to site*

* fr £13 fr £13 fr £13

Open all year Last arrival 22.00hrs Last departure noon

A peaceful and relaxing park situated in the heart of the south Lincolnshire countryside, yet only a mile from the centre of Boston. The enthusiastic, hands-on owners have done a superb job in upgrading the facilities. The park offers quality toilet facilities, 22 electric hook ups and hardstandings, and tents are welcome in a separate grassy area. Seasonal touring pitches. A 2 acre site with 22 touring pitches, 15 hardstandings.

Leisure: **Facilities:** **Services:** **Within 3 miles:** **Notes:** Dogs welcome but must be on leads at all times. Tea house & sun terrace

CLEETHORPES

77% Thorpe Park Holiday Centre

DN35 0PW

☎ 01472 813395 📠 01472 812146

e-mail: luke.cullen@bourne-leisure.co.uk

dir: *Take unclass road off A180 at Cleethorpes, signed Humberstone & Holiday Park*

* £10-£86 £10-£86 £10-£58

Open mid Mar-Oct (rs mid Mar-May & Sep-Oct some facilities may be reduced) Last arrival anytime Last departure 10.00hrs

A large static site with touring facilities, including fully-serviced pitches and a new additional toilet block, adjacent to the beach. This holiday centre offers excellent recreational and leisure activities, including an indoor pool with bar, bowling greens, crazy golf, and a games area. A 300 acre site with 119 touring pitches, 68 hardstandings and 281 statics.

Leisure: **Facilities:** **Services:** **Within 3 miles:**

Notes: Max 2 dogs per group, no commercial vehicles. Pitch & putt, roller ring, fishing lakes. Wi-fi

MABLETHORPE

75% Golden Sands Holiday Park

Quebec Rd LN12 1QJ

☎ 01507 477871 01507 472066

e-mail: naomi.mcintosh@bourne-leisure.co.uk

dir: *From centre of Mablethorpe turn left on seafront road towards north end. Site on left*

* £6-£66 £6-£66 £6-£38

Open mid Mar-Oct Last arrival anytime Last departure 10.00hrs

A large, well-equipped seaside holiday park with separate touring facilities on two sites, including fully modernised toilets. The first floor entertainment rooms are only accessible via stairs (no lifts). Seasonal touring pitches available. A 23 acre site with 214 touring pitches, 20 hardstandings and 1500 statics.

Leisure:

Facilities:

Services:

Within 3 miles:

Notes: Maximum of 2 dogs per group, certain dog breeds banned. Mini bowling alley, snooker/pool, indoor fun palace. Wi-fi

E4 CHINGFORD

►►► 81% Lee Valley Campsite

Sewardstone Rd E4 7RA

☎ 020 8529 5689 020 8559 4070

e-mail: scs@leevalleypark.org.uk

dir: *M25 junct 26, A112. Site signed*

Open Apr-Oct Last arrival 21.00hrs Last departure noon

Overlooking King George's Reservoir and close to Epping Forest, this park has excellent modern facilities and a very peaceful atmosphere. A bus calls at the site hourly to take passengers to the nearest tube station, and Enfield is easily accessible. This impressive park is maintained to a high standard. A 12 acre site with 100 touring pitches, 20 hardstandings and 43 statics.

Leisure:

Facilities:

Services:

Within 3 miles:

Notes: Under 18s must be accompanied by an adult

N9 EDMONTON

►►► 84% Lee Valley Camping & Caravan Park

Meridian Way N9 0AR

☎ 020 8803 6900 020 8884 4975

e-mail: leisurecomplex@leevalleypark.org.uk

dir: *M25 junct 25, A10 S, 1st left onto A1055, approx 5m to Leisure Complex. From A406 (North Circular), N on A1010, left after 0.25m, right (Pickets Lock Ln)*

Open all year Last arrival 22.00hrs Last departure noon

A pleasant, open site within easy reach of London yet peacefully located close to two large reservoirs. The very good toilet facilities are beautifully kept by dedicated wardens, and the site has the advantage of being adjacent to a restaurant and bar, and a multi-screen cinema. A 4.5 acre site with 160 touring pitches, 41 hardstandings.

Leisure:

Facilities:

Services:

Within 3 miles:

Notes: No commercial vehicles. Golf course

SOUTHPORT

84% Riverside Holiday Park

Southport New Rd PR9 8DF

☎ 01704 228886 01704 505886

e-mail: reception@harrisonleisureuk.com

dir: *M6 junct 27, A5209 towards Parbold/ Burscough, right onto A59. Left onto A565 at lights in Tarleton. Continue to dual carriageway. At rdbt straight across, site 1m on left*

* £15-£22 £15-£22 £10-£29

Open Mar-6 Jan Last arrival 17.00hrs Last departure 11.00hrs

A large, spacious park with a lively family entertainment complex for cabaret, dancing and theme nights. Children have their own club and entertainer plus games and food. A superb health and leisure centre next door is available at an extra charge. Seasonal touring pitches available. An 80 acre site with 260 touring pitches, 130 hardstandings and 355 statics.

Leisure:

Facilities:

Services:

Within 3 miles: **Notes:** Dogs must be kept on leads & one car per pitch

SOUTHPORT

►►► 76% Hurlston Hall Country Caravan Park

Southport Rd L40 8HB

☎ 01704 841064 📠 01704 841404

e-mail: enquiries@hurlstonhallcaravanpark.co.uk

dir: *On A570, 3m from Ormskirk towards Southport*

* £15-£22.50 £15-£22.50

Open Etr-Oct Last arrival 20.30hrs (Last arrival time 18.30hrs at weekends) Last departure 17.00hrs

A peaceful tree-lined touring park next to a static site in attractive countryside about 10 minutes' drive from Southport. The park is maturing well, with growing trees and a coarse fishing lake. No dogs permitted. A 5 acre site with 60 touring pitches and 68 statics.

Leisure:

Facilities:

Services:

Within 3 miles:

Notes: No tents. Coarse fishing, golf facilities

BARNEY

►►►► 91% The Old Brick Kilns

Little Barney Ln NR21 0NL

☎ 01328 878305 📠 01328 878948

e-mail: enquiries@old-brick-kilns.co.uk

dir: *From A148 (Fakenham-Cromer) follow brown tourist signs to Barney, left into Little Barney Ln. Site at end of lane*

* £14.50-£26 £14.50-£26 £12.50-£22

Open mid Mar-6 Jan (rs Low season bar food/takeaway selected nights only) Last arrival 21.00hrs Last departure noon

A secluded and peaceful park approached via a leafy country lane. The park is on two levels with its own boating and fishing pool and many mature trees. Excellent, well-planned toilet facilities can be found in two blocks, and there is a short dog walk. Due to a narrow access road, no arrivals are accepted until after 1pm. A 12.73 acre site with 65 touring pitches, 65 hardstandings.

Leisure: Facilities: Services: Within 3 miles:

Notes: No gazebos. Outdoor draughts, chess, family games. Wi-fi

BELTON

67% Wild Duck Holiday Park

Howards Common NR31 9NE

☎ 01493 780268 01493 782308

dir: *From A47 towards Gt Yarmouth take A143 towards Beccles. Turn right at Burgh Castle, right at T-junct, left at next T-junct, site 200mtrs on right*

Open mid Mar-Oct (rs mid Mar-May & Sep-Oct some facilities may be reduced) Last arrival 22.30hrs Last departure 10.00hrs

This a large holiday complex with plenty to do for all ages both indoors and out. This level grassy site is set in a forest with small cleared areas for tourers and well laid out facilities. Clubs for children and teenagers, sporting activities and evening shows all add to the fun of a stay here. A 97 acre site with 120 touring pitches and 365 statics.

Leisure:

Facilities:

Services:

Within 3 miles:

Notes: Certain dog breeds banned. Wi-fi

BELTON

►►►► 87% Rose Farm Touring & Camping Park

Stepshort NR31 9JS

☎ 01493 780896 01493 780896

dir: *Follow signs to Belton off A143, right at lane signed Stepshort, site 1st on right*

Open all year

A former railway line is the setting for this very peaceful site which enjoys rural views and is beautifully presented throughout. The ever-improving toilet facilities are spotlessly clean and inviting to use, and the park is brightened with many flower and herb beds. Customer care is truly exceptional. A 10 acre site with 80 touring pitches, 15 hardstandings.

Leisure:

Facilities:

Services:

Within 3 miles:

Notes: No dog fouling. Wi-fi

BURGH CASTLE

77% Breydon Water

Butt Ln NR31 9QB

☎ 0871 664 9710

e-mail: breydon.water@park-resorts.com

dir: *From Gt Yarmouth on A12 towards Lowestoft over 2 rdbts. Follow Burgh Castle sign. Right at lights signed Diss & Beccles. 1.5m, right signed Burgh Castle & Belton. At mini rdbt right onto Stepshort. Site on right*

Open Mar-Oct Last arrival 19.00hrs

This large park has two village areas just a short walk apart. Choose Yare Village for family fun and superb entertainment, and Bure Village for a quieter base. Although the villages are separated, guests are more than welcome to use facilities at both. Both villages have touring areas with modern, well maintained toilets, and tents are welcome. They are just a short drive from the bright lights of Yarmouth and the unique Norfolk Broads. 176 touring pitches and 327 statics.

Leisure:
Facilities:
Services:
Within 3 miles:

CLIPPESBY

►►►►► 90% Clippesby Hall

Hall Ln NR29 3BL

☎ 01493 367800 01493 367809

e-mail: holidays@clippesby.com

web: www.clippesby.com

dir: *From A47 follow tourist signs for The Broads. At Acle rdbt take A1064, after 2m left onto B1152, 0.5m turn left opposite village sign, site 400yds on right*

Open Etr-end Oct (rs Etr-Whit no swimming/tennis. Pub/café BH wknds) Last arrival 17.30hrs Last departure 11.00hrs

A lovely country house estate with secluded pitches hidden among the trees or in sheltered glades. The toilet facilities are appointed to a high standard, providing a wide choice of cubicle. Amenities include a café, clubhouse and family crazy-golf. There four pine lodges and 13 holiday cottages available for holiday lets. A 30 acre site with 120 touring pitches, 9 hardstandings.

Leisure: **Facilities:** **Services:** **Within 3 miles:**

Notes: Dogs must be kept on leads. Bicycle hire & mini golf. Wi-fi

CROMER

►►► 77% Forest Park

Northrepps Rd NR27 0JR

☎ 01263 513290 📠 01263 511992

e-mail: info@forest-park.co.uk

dir: *A140 from Norwich, left at T-junct signed Cromer, right signed Northrepps, right then immediate left, left at T-junct, site on right*

Open 15 Mar-15 Jan Last arrival 21.00hrs Last departure 11.00hrs

Surrounded by forest, this gently sloping park offers a wide choice of pitches. Visitors have the use of a heated indoor swimming pool, and a large clubhouse with entertainment. A 100 acre site with 344 touring pitches and 372 statics.

Leisure:

Facilities:

Services:

Within 3 miles:

Notes: BMX track, hair salon. Wi-fi

GREAT HOCKHAM

►►► 75% Thetford Forest Camping & Caravanning Club Site

Puddledock Farm IP24 1PA

☎ 01953 498455

dir: *Off A1075 between Norwich & Cambridge*

Open all year Last arrival 21.00hrs Last departure noon

This expansive site on the edge of Thetford Forest occupies a central location in East Anglia, providing a multitude of touring options. The pitches are generously proportioned and well sheltered. There is a small fishing lake on site. 80 touring pitches, 80 hardstandings.

Leisure:

Facilities:

Services:

Within 3 miles:

Notes: Site gates closed 23.00hrs-07.00hrs

GREAT YARMOUTH

84% Vauxhall Holiday Park

4 Acle New Rd NR30 1TB

☎ 01493 857231 01493 331122

e-mail: info@vauxhallholidays.co.uk

web: www.vauxhall-holiday-park.co.uk

dir: *On A47 approaching Great Yarmouth*

Open Etr, mid May-Sep & Oct half term Last arrival 21.00hrs Last departure 10.00hrs

A very large holiday complex with plenty of entertainment and access to beach, river, estuary, lake and the A47. The touring pitches are laid out in four separate areas, each with its own amenity block, and all are arranged around the main entertainment. A 40 acre site with 220 touring pitches and 421 statics.

Leisure:

Facilities:

Services:

Within 3 miles:

Notes: No pets. Children's pool, sauna, solarium, fitness centre

HUNSTANTON

86% Searles Leisure Resort

South Beach Rd PE36 5BB

☎ 01485 534211 01485 533815

e-mail: bookings@searles.co.uk

web: www.searles.co.uk

dir: *A149 from King's Lynn to Hunstanton. At rdbt follow signs for South Beach. Straight on at 2nd rdbt. Site on left*

* £14-£44 £14-£44 £14-£42

Open all year (rs 25 Dec & Feb-May limited entertainment & restaurant) Last arrival 20.45hrs Last departure 11.00hrs

Large seaside holiday complex with well-managed facilities, adjacent to the beach. Tourers have their own areas, including two excellent toilet blocks, and pitches are marked by small shrubs for privacy. The bars and entertainment, restaurant, bistro and takeaway, golf, fishing and bowling green make this park popular throughout the year. A 50 acre site with 332 touring pitches, 100 hardstandings and 460 statics.

Leisure: Facilities: Services: Within 3 miles: Notes: No dangerous dog breeds. Hire shop, beauty salon. Wi-fi

SANDRINGHAM

►►►► 87% Sandringham Camping & Caravanning Club Site

The Sandringham Estate, Double Lodges
PE35 6EA

☎ 01485 542555

dir: *From A148 onto B1440 signed West Newton. Follow signs to site. From A149 turn left & follow site signs*

Open 12 Feb-23 Nov Last arrival 21.00hrs Last departure noon

A prestige park, very well landscaped and laid out in mature woodland, with toilets and other buildings blending in with the scenery. There are plenty of walks from the site, and this is a good touring base for the rest of Norfolk. A 28 acre site with 275 touring pitches, 2 hardstandings.

Leisure:

Facilities:

Services:

Within 3 miles:

Notes: Site gates closed 23.00hrs-07.00hrs

SCRATBY

►►► 82% Scratby Hall Caravan Park

NR29 3SR

☎ 01493 730283

dir: *5m N of Great Yarmouth. Exit A149 onto B1159, site signed*

Open Spring BH-mid Sep Last arrival 22.00hrs Last departure noon

A neatly-maintained site with a popular children's play area, well-equipped shop and outdoor swimming pool with sun terrace. The toilets are kept very clean. The beach and the Norfolk Broads are close by. A 5 acre site with 108 touring pitches.

Leisure:

Facilities:

Services:

Within 3 miles:

Notes: No commercial vehicles. Food preparation room

SEA PALLING

►►► 75% Golden Beach Holiday Centre

Beach Rd NR12 0AL

☎ 01692 598269

e-mail: goldenbeach@keme.co.uk

dir: *From A149 at Stalham follow signs to Sea Palling. From Stalham Rd take Beach Rd, site on left*

* £13-£17 £13-£17 ▲ £13-£17

Open 20 Mar-26 Oct Last arrival 20.00hrs Last departure 10.00hrs

Just a few yards from the sea, Golden Beach is ideally located for family holidays. The touring field is well grassed, and served by its own toilet block offering standard facilities. There is a small friendly bar, plus café, pool room and shop, all housed in modern buildings. Sea Palling is a quiet village away from, but close to, seaside attractions. A 6 acre site with 37 touring pitches and 111 statics.

Leisure:

Facilities:

Services:

Within 3 miles:

Notes: No boats or jet skis

TRIMINGHAM

►►► 70% Woodland Leisure Park

NR11 8AL

☎ 01263 579208 01263 576477

e-mail: info@woodland-park.co.uk

web: www.woodland-park.co.uk

dir: *4m SE on B1159 (coast road)*

£19-£29 £19-£29 ▲ £15-£20

Open Mar-Dec Last arrival 23.00hrs Last departure noon

A secluded woodland site in an open enclosure, close to the sea but well sheltered from the winds by tall trees. Facilities include two bars, a restaurant, an indoor swimming pool, bowling green and sauna, and entertainment is provided in the clubhouse. Seasonal touring pitches available. A 55 acre site with 20 touring pitches and 230 statics.

Leisure:

Facilities:

Services:

Within 3 miles:

Notes: Wi-fi

WEST RUNTON

►►►► 85% West Runton Camping & Caravanning Club Site

Holgate Ln NR27 9NW

☎ 01263 837544

dir: *From King's Lynn on A148 towards West Runton. Left at Roman Camp Inn. Site track on right at crest of hill, 0.5m to site opposite National Trust sign*

Open 2 Apr-2 Nov Last arrival 21.00hrs Last departure noon

A lovely, well-kept site with some gently sloping pitches on pleasantly undulating ground. This peaceful park is surrounded on three sides by woodland, with the fourth side open to fields and the coast beyond. The very well equipped family rooms and toilet blocks are excellent. A 15 acre site with 200 touring pitches, 3 hardstandings.

Leisure:

Facilities:

Services:

Within 3 miles:

Notes: Site gates closed 23.00hrs-07.00hrs

BAMBURGH

►►►► 74% Waren Caravan Park

Waren Mill NE70 7EE

☎ 01668 214366 01668 214224

e-mail: waren@meadowhead.co.uk

dir: *2m E of town. From A1 onto B1342 signed Bamburgh. Take unclass road past Waren Mill, signed Budle*

* £13-£23 £13-£23 £13-£27

Open Apr-Oct Last arrival 20.00hrs Last departure noon

Attractive seaside site with footpath access to the beach, surrounded by a slightly sloping grassy embankment giving shelter to caravans. The park offers excellent facilities including several family bathrooms. There are also wooden wigwams to rent. A 4 acre site with 180 touring pitches, 24 hardstandings and 300 statics.

Leisure:

Facilities:

Services:

Within 3 miles:

Notes: 100 acres of private heathland. Wi-fi

BELLINGHAM

►►►► 84% Bellingham Brown Rigg Camping & Caravanning Club Site

Brown Rigg NE48 2JY

☎ 01434 220175

dir: *From A69 take A68 N. Then B6318 to Chollerford & B6320 to Bellingham. Pass Forestry Commission land, site 0.5m S of Bellingham*

Open Apr-Oct Last arrival 21.00hrs Last departure noon

A beautiful and peaceful site set in the glorious Northumberland National Park. This is a perfect base for exploring this undiscovered part of England, and it is handily placed for visiting the beautiful Northumberland coast. The site has been refurbished to a very good standard. A 5 acre site with 64 touring pitches, 64 hardstandings.

Leisure:

Facilities:

Services:

Within 3 miles:

Notes: Site gates closed 23.00hrs-07.00hrs. Bike hire, fishing, rock climbing, horse riding. Wi-fi

BERWICK-UPON-TWEED

74% Haggerston Castle

Beal TD15 2PA

☎ 01289 381333 01289 381433

e-mail: sharon.lee@bourne-leisure.co.uk

dir: *On A1, 7m S of Berwick-upon-Tweed, site signed*

* £12-£74 £12-£74

Open mid Mar-Oct (rs mid Mar-May & Sep-Oct some facilities may be reduced) Last arrival anytime Last departure 10.00hrs

A large holiday centre with a very well equipped touring park, offering comprehensive holiday activities. The entertainment complex contains amusements for the whole family, and there are several bars, an adventure playground, boating on the lake, a children's club, a 9-hole golf course, tennis courts, and various eating outlets. Seasonal touring pitches available. A 100 acre site with 150 touring pitches, 150 hardstandings and 1200 statics.

Leisure:

Facilities:

Services:

Within 3 miles:

Notes: No tents. Wi-fi

CRASTER

►►► 78% Dunstan Hill Camping & Caravanning Club Site

Dunstan Hill, Dunstan NE66 3TQ

☎ 01665 576310

dir: *From A1, just N of Alnwick, take B1340 signed Seahouses. Continue to T-junct at Criston Bank, turn right. 2nd right signed Embleton. Right at x-rds then 1st left signed Craster*

Open 2 Apr-2 Nov Last arrival 21.00hrs Last departure noon

An immaculately maintained site with pleasant landscaping, close to the beach and Craster harbour. The historic town of Alnwick is nearby, as is the ruined Dunstanburgh Castle. A 14 acre site with 150 touring pitches, 20 hardstandings.

Leisure:

Facilities:

Services:

Within 3 miles:

Notes: Site gates closed 23.00hrs-07.00hrs

HEXHAM

►►► 65% Hexham Racecourse Caravan Site

Hexham Racecourse NE46 2JP

☎ 01434 606847 & 606881

01434 605814

e-mail: hexrace.caravan@uku.co.uk

dir: *From Hexham take B6305 signed Allendale/Alston. Left in 3m signed to racecourse. Site 1.5m on right*

* £12-£15 £12-£15 fr £8

Open May-Sep Last arrival 20.00hrs Last departure noon

A part-level and part-sloping grassy site situated on a racecourse overlooking Hexhamshire Moors. The facilities are functional. A 4 acre site with 40 touring pitches.

Leisure:

Facilities:

Services:

Within 3 miles:

NORTH SEATON

71% Sandy Bay

NE63 9YD

0871 664 9764

e-mail: sandy.bay@park-resorts.com

dir: *From A1 at Seaton Burn take A19 signed Tyne Tunnel. Then A189 signed Ashington, approx 8m, at rdbt right onto B1334 towards Newbiggin-by-the-Sea. Site on right*

* £7-£30 £7-£30

Open Mar-Oct Last departure 10.00hrs

A beach-side holiday park on the outskirts of the small village of North Seaton, within easy reach of Newcastle. The site is handily placed for exploring the magnificent coastline and countryside of Northumberland, but for those who do not wish to travel it offers the full range of holiday centre attractions, both for parents and children. 48 touring pitches and 396 statics.

Leisure:

Facilities:

Services:

Within 3 miles:

Notes: Koi carp lake

RADCLIFFE ON TRENT

►►► 74% Thornton's Holt Camping Park

Stragglethorpe Rd, Stragglethorpe NG12 2JZ

0115 933 2125 & 933 4204

0115 933 3318

e-mail: camping@thorntons-holt.co.uk

web: www.thorntons-holt.co.uk

dir: *Take A52, 3m E of Nottingham. Turn S at lights towards Cropwell Bishop. Site 0.5m on left. Or A46 SE of Nottingham. N at lights. Site 2.5m on right*

Open Apr-6 Nov Last arrival 20.00hrs Last departure 13.00hrs

A well-run family site in former meadowland, with pitches located among young trees and bushes for a rural atmosphere and outlook. The toilets are housed in converted farm buildings, and an indoor swimming pool is a popular attraction. A 13 acre site with 155 touring pitches, 35 hardstandings.

Leisure:

Facilities:

Services:

Within 3 miles:

Notes: Noise curfew at 22.00hrs. Pub & restaurant (150mtrs)

TEVERSAL

►►►►► 85% Teversal Camping & Caravanning Club Site

Silverhill Ln NG17 3JJ

☎ 01623 551838

dir: *M1 junct 28, A38 towards Mansfield. Left at lights onto B6027. At hill top straight over at lights, left at Peacock Hotel. Right onto B6014, left at Craven Arms, site on left*

Open all year Last arrival 21.00hrs Last departure noon

A top notch park with excellent purpose-built facilities and innovative, hands-on owners. Each pitch is spacious, the excellent new toilet facilities are state-of-the-art, and there are views of and access to the countryside and nearby Silverhill Community Woods. The attention to detail and all-round quality are truly exceptional. A 6 acre site with 126 touring pitches, 58 hardstandings and 1 statics.

Leisure: **Facilities:**
Services:
Within 3 miles:
Notes: Site gates closed 23.00hrs-07.00hrs. Car hire available. Wi-fi

BANBURY

►►►► 82% Barnstones Caravan & Camping Site

Great Bourton OX17 1QU

☎ 01295 750289

dir: *Take A423 from Banbury signed Southam. In 3m turn right signed Gt Bourton/Cropredy, site 100yds on right*

£11-£13 £11-£13 £7-£10

Open all year

Popular, neatly laid-out site with plenty of hardstandings, some fully serviced pitches, a smart up-to-date toilet block, and excellent rally facilities. Well run by personable owner. A 3 acre site with 49 touring pitches, 44 hardstandings.

Leisure:
Facilities:
Services:
Within 3 miles:
Notes:

BLETCHINGDON

►►►► 79% Diamond Farm Caravan & Camping Park

Islip Rd OX5 3DR

☎ 01869 350909

e-mail: warden@diamondpark.co.uk

dir: *From M40 junct 9 onto A34 S for 3m, then B4027 to Bletchingdon. Site 1m on left*

Open all year Last arrival dusk Last departure 11.00hrs

A well-run, quiet rural site in good level surroundings, and ideal for touring the Cotswolds. Situated seven miles north of Oxford in the heart of the Thames Valley. This popular park has excellent facilities, and offers a heated outdoor swimming pool and a games room for children. A 3 acre site with 37 touring pitches, 13 hardstandings.

Leisure:

Facilities:

Services:

Within 3 miles:

Notes: Wi-fi

BLETCHINGDON

►►► 85% Greenhill Leisure Park

Greenhill Farm, Station Rd OX5 3BQ

☎ 01869 351600 01869 350918

e-mail: info@greenhill-leisure-park.co.uk

web: www.greenhill-leisure-park.co.uk

dir: *M40 junct 9, A34 south for 3m. Take B4027 to Bletchingdon. Site 0.5m after village on left*

£12-£15 £12-£15 £12-£15

Open all year (rs Oct-Mar no dogs, shop & games room closed) Last arrival 21.00hrs Last departure noon

An all-year round park set in open countryside near the village of Bletchingdon. Fishing is available in the nearby river, and the park has its own farm shop. It makes an ideal base for touring the Cotswolds and Oxford. A 7 acre site with 61 touring pitches, 25 hardstandings.

Leisure:

Facilities:

Services:

Within 3 miles:

Notes: No camp fires. Pets corner. Wi-fi

CHARLBURY

►►►► 83%

Cotswold View Touring Park

Enstone Rd OX7 3JH

☎ 01608 810314 🖷 01608 811891

e-mail: bookings@gfwiddows.co.uk

dir: *From A44 in Enstone take B4022 towards Charlbury. Follow site signs. Site 1m from Charlbury.*

Open Etr or Apr-Oct Last arrival 21.00hrs Last departure noon

A good Cotswold site, well screened and with attractive views across the countryside. The toilet facilities include fully-equipped family rooms and bathrooms, and there are spacious, sheltered pitches, some with hardstandings. Breakfast and takeaway food available from the shop. A 10 acre site with 125 touring pitches.

Leisure:

Facilities:

Services:

Within 3 miles:

Notes: Off licence, skittle alley, chess, boules

HENLEY-ON-THAMES

►►►► 82%

Swiss Farm Touring & Camping

Marlow Rd RG9 2HY

☎ 01491 573419

e-mail: enquiries@swissfarmcamping.co.uk

web: www.swissfarmcamping.co.uk

dir: *On A4155, N of Henley, next left after rugby club, towards Marlow*

* £11-£21 £11-£21 £11-£18

Open Mar-Oct Last arrival 21.00hrs Last departure noon

A conveniently-located site within a few minutes walk of Henley, and ideal for those visiting Henley during Regatta Week. Visitors are invited to fish in the park's well-stocked lake, which is set in a secluded wooded area. Facilities and general maintenance are to a very good standard. A 6 acre site with 140 touring pitches, 20 hardstandings and 6 statics.

Leisure:

Facilities:

Services:

Within 3 miles:

Notes: No groups. Wi-fi

STANDLAKE

►►►►► 95%

Lincoln Farm Park Oxfordshire

High St OX29 7RH

☎ 01865 300239 📠 01865 300127

e-mail: info@lincolnfarmpark.co.uk

web: www.lincolnfarmpark.co.uk

dir: *In village off A415 between Abingdon & Witney, 5m SE of Witney*

Open Feb-Nov Last arrival 20.00hrs Last departure noon

Run by enthusiast owners this attractively landscaped park is in a quiet village setting only a mile from the River Thames, with superb facilities and a high standard of maintenance. Family rooms, fully-serviced pitches, a café, two indoor swimming pools and a fully-equipped gym are part of the amenities. A 9 acre site with 90 touring pitches, 75 hardstandings.

Leisure: **Facilities:** **Services:** **Within 3 miles:**

Notes: No gazebos, dogs must be kept on leads, no noise after 23.00hrs. Putting green, outdoor chess. Wi-fi

GREETHAM

►►► 86%

Rutland Caravan & Camping

Park Ln LE15 7FN

☎ 01572 813520

e-mail: info@rutlandcaravanandcamping.co.uk

dir: *From A1 onto B668 towards Greetham. Before Greetham turn right at x-rds, 2nd left to site*

Open all year

A pretty caravan park built to a high specification, and surrounded by well-planted banks which will provide good screening. The spacious grassy site is close to the Viking Way and other footpath networks, and well sited for visiting Rutland Water and the many picturesque villages in the area. A 5 acre site with 130 touring pitches, 65 hardstandings.

Leisure:

Facilities:

Services:

Within 3 miles:

Notes: Wi-fi

BRIDGNORTH

►►►► 92%

Stanmore Hall Touring Park

Stourbridge Rd WV15 6DT

01746 761761 01746 768069

e-mail: stanmore@morris-leisure

dir: *2m E of Bridgnorth on A458*

Open all year Last arrival 20.00hrs Last departure noon

An excellent park in peaceful surroundings offering outstanding facilities. The pitches, many of them fully serviced, are arranged around the lake in Stanmore Hall, home of the Midland Motor Museum. Handy for touring Ironbridge and the Severn Valley Railway, while Bridgnorth itself is an attractive old market town. A 12.5 acre site with 131 touring pitches, 53 hardstandings.

Leisure:

Facilities:

Services:

Within 3 miles:

Notes: Max of 2 dogs

SHREWSBURY

►►►► 93%

Oxon Hall Touring Park

Welshpool Rd SY3 5FB

01743 340868 01743 340869

e-mail: oxon@morris-leisure.co.uk

dir: *Exit A5 (ring road) at junct with A458. Site shares entrance with 'Oxon Park & Ride'*

Open all year Last arrival 21.00hrs

A delightful park with quality facilities, and a choice of grass and fully-serviced pitches. An adults-only section is very popular with those wanting a peaceful holiday, and there is an inviting patio area next to reception and the shop, overlooking a small lake. This site is ideally located for visiting Shrewsbury and the surrounding countryside, and there is always a warm welcome. A 15 acre site with 124 touring pitches, 72 hardstandings and 42 statics.

Leisure:

Facilities:

Services:

Within 3 miles:

WEM

►►► 78%

Lower Lacon Caravan Park

SY4 5RP

☎ 01939 232376 01939 233606

e-mail: info@llcp.co.uk

web: www.llcp.co.uk

dir: *Take A49 to B5065. Site 3m on right*

* £16-£26.50 £16-£26.50 £16-£26.50

Open Apr-Oct (rs Nov-Mar club wknds only, toilets closed if frost) Last arrival 20.00hrs Last departure 16.00hrs

A large, spacious park with lively club facilities and an entertainments barn, set safely away from the main road. The park is particularly suitable for families, with an outdoor swimming pool and farm animals. A 48 acre site with 270 touring pitches, 30 hardstandings and 50 statics.

Leisure:

Facilities:

Services:

Within 3 miles:

Notes: No skateboards, no commercial vehicles. Crazy golf

BATH

►►►► 86%

Newton Mill Holiday Park

Newton Rd BA2 9JF

☎ 01225 333909

e-mail: enquiries@newtonmillpark.co.uk

dir: *From Bath W on A4 to rdbt by Globe Inn, immediate left, site 1m on left*

Open all year Last arrival 21.00hrs Last departure 11.00hrs

An attractive, high quality park set in a sheltered valley and surrounded by woodland, with a stream running through. It offers excellent toilet facilities with private cubicles and rooms, and there is an appealing restaurant and bar offering a wide choice of menus throughout the year. The city is easily accessible by bus or via the Bristol to Bath cycle path. A 42 acre site with 212 touring pitches, 85 hardstandings.

Leisure:

Facilities:

Services:

Within 3 miles:

Notes: Fishing, satellite TV hook ups

BREAN

86% Warren Farm Holiday Centre

Brean Sands TA8 2RP

☎ 01278 751227

e-mail: enquiries@warren-farm.co.uk

dir: *M5 junct 22 , B3140 through Burnham-on-Sea to Berrow & Brean. Site 1.5m past Brean Leisure Park*

* £7-£16 £7-£16 £7-£16

Open Apr-Oct Last arrival 20.00hrs Last departure noon

A large family-run holiday park, with excellent facilities, close to the beach, and divided into several fields each with its own designated facilities. Pitches are spacious and level, and enjoy panoramic views of the Mendip Hills and Brean Down. A bar and restaurant are part of the complex, which provide entertainment for all the family, and there is also separate entertainment for children. A 100 acre site with 575 touring pitches and 800 statics.

Leisure: **Facilities:** **Services:** **Within 3 miles:**

Notes: No commercial vehicles. Fishing lake & ponds, indoor play area. Wi-fi

BREAN

►►►► 81% Northam Farm Touring Park

TA8 2SE

☎ 01278 751244 01278 751150

e-mail: enquiries@northamfarm.co.uk

dir: *From M5 junct 22 to Burnham-on-Sea. In Brean, Northam Farm on right 0.5m past Brean Leisure Park*

* £8.75-£22.50 £8.75-£22.50 £8.75-£19

Open Mar-Oct (rs Mar & Oct shop/cafe/takeaway open limited hours) Last arrival 20.00hrs Last departure 10.30hrs

An attractive site a short walk from the sea and a long sandy beach. This quality park also has lots of children's play areas, and also runs the Seagull Inn about 600 yards away, which includes a restaurant and entertainment. There is a fishing lake on the site which proves very popular. A DVD of the site is now available free of charge. A 30 acre site with 350 touring pitches, 252 hardstandings.

Leisure: **Facilities:** **Services:** **Within 3 miles:**

Notes: Families & couples only. No motorcycles or commercial vans

BRIDGWATER

75% Mill Farm Caravan & Camping Park

Fiddington TA5 1JQ

☎ 01278 732286

web: www.millfarm.biz

dir: *From Bridgwater take A39 W, left at Cannington rdbt, 2m, right just beyond Apple Inn towards Fiddington. Follow camping signs*

* £16-£20 £16-£20 £16-£20

Open all year Last arrival 23.00hrs Last departure 10.00hrs

A large holiday park with plenty for all the family, including horse riding, boating lake and gym. There is also a clubhouse with bar and full entertainment programme in the main season. Although a lively and busy park in the main season the park also offers a much quieter environment at other times, although some activities and entertainment may not be available. A 6 acre site with 125 touring pitches.

Leisure:

Facilities:

Services:

Within 3 miles:

Notes: Canoeing, pool table, trampolines, pony rides. Wi-fi

BURNHAM-ON-SEA

79% Burnham-on-Sea Holiday Village

Marine Dr TA8 1LA

☎ 01278 783391 01278 793776

e-mail: elaine.organ@bourne-leisure.co.uk

dir: *M5 junct 22. Left 1st rdbt onto A38 towards Highbridge. Over mini rdbt, right onto B3139 to Burnham. After Total Garage left onto Marine Drive. Park 400yds on left*

* £14-£96 £14-£96 £14-£86

Open mid Mar-Oct (rs Mid Mar-May & Sep-Oct facilities may be reduced) Last arrival anytime Last departure 10.00hrs

A large family-orientated holiday village complex with a separate touring park containing 43 super pitches. There is a wide range of activities including excellent pools, plus bars, restaurants and entertainment for all the family. The coarse fishing lake is very popular, and Burnham is only half a mile away. A 94 acre site with 72 touring pitches, 44 hardstandings and 700 statics.

Leisure:

Facilities:

Services:

Within 3 miles:

Notes: No commercial vehicles. Wi-fi

BURTLE

► 75% Orchard Camping

Ye Olde Burtle Inn, Catcott Rd TA7 8NG

☎ 01278 722269 & 722123

01278 722269

e-mail: food@theinn.eu

dir: *M5 junct 23, A39, in approx 4m left onto unclass road to Burtle, site by pub in village centre*

Open all year Last arrival anytime

A simple campsite set in an orchard at the rear of a lovely 17th-century family inn in the heart of the Somerset Levels. The restaurant offers a wide range of meals, and breakfast can be pre-ordered by campers. A shower and disabled toilet have been added and these facilities are available to campers outside pub opening hours. Free internet access and Wi-fi available. A 0.75 acre site with 30 touring pitches.

Leisure:

Facilities:

Services:

Within 3 miles:

Notes: Bicycle & tent hire, sleeping bags & equipment

CHARD

►►► 87% Alpine Grove Touring Park

Forton TA20 4HD

☎ 01460 63479 01460 63479

e-mail: stay@alpinegrovetouringpark.com

dir: *Exit A30 between Chard & Crewkerne towards Cricket St Thomas, follow signs. Site 2m on right*

* £11-£19.50 £11-£19.50 £11-£19.50

Open 1 wk before Etr-Sep Last arrival 21.00hrs Last departure 10.30hrs

A warm welcome awaits at this quiet wooded park with both hardstandings and grass pitches, close to Cricket St Thomas Wildlife Park. Families particularly enjoy the small swimming pool and terrace in summer. Log cabins are also available for hire. An 8.5 acre site with 40 touring pitches, 15 hardstandings.

Leisure:

Facilities:

Services:

Within 3 miles:

Notes: No open fires, dogs must be kept on leads. Dog-sitting service, fire pits to hire. Wi-fi

CHEDDAR

82% Broadway House Holiday Park

Axbridge Rd BS27 3DB

01934 742610 01934 744950

e-mail: enquiries@broadwayhousepark.co.uk

dir: *From M5 junct 22 follow signs to Cheddar Gorge & Caves (8m). Site midway between Cheddar & Axbridge on A371*

Open Mar-Oct (rs Mar-end May & Oct bar & pool closed, limited shop hours) Last arrival 23.00hrs Last departure noon

A well-equipped holiday park on the slopes of the Mendips with a great range of activities. This is a busy and lively park in the main holiday periods, but can be peaceful off-peak. Broadway has its own competition standard BMX track, which is used for National and European Championships, plus skateboard park and many other activities. The slightly terraced pitches face south. 64 seasonal touring pitches available. A 30 acre site with 345 touring pitches, 70 hardstandings.

Leisure: **Facilities:** **Services:** **Within 3 miles:** **Notes:** Children to be supervised at all times. Table tennis. Wi-fi

CREWKERNE

►►► 80% Oathill Farm Touring and Camping Site

Oathill, Clapton TA18 8PZ

01460 30234 01460 30234

e-mail: oathillfarm@btconnect.com

dir: *From Crewkerne take B3165. Site on left just after Clapton*

£17.50-£25.50 £17.50-£25.50 £13-£22.50

Open all year Last arrival 20.00hrs Last departure noon

This small peaceful park is located on the borders of Somerset and Devon, with the Jurassic coast of Lyme Regis, Charmouth and Bridport only a short drive away. The new, modern facilities are spotless and there are hardstandings and fully-serviced pitches available. Lucy's Tea Room serves breakfast and meals. A 9 acre site with 13 touring pitches, 13 hardstandings and 3 statics.

Facilities:

Services:

Within 3 miles:

Notes: No washing lines, no quad bikes, no noise after 23.00hrs. Separate recreational areas, landscaped fish ponds

CROWCOMBE

►►►► 81% Quantock Orchard Caravan Park

Flaxpool TA4 4AW

☎ 01984 618618

e-mail: member@flaxpool.freeserve.co.uk

web: www.quantock-orchard.co.uk

dir: *Take A358 from Taunton, signed Minehead & Williton. In 8m turn left just past Flaxpool Garage. Park immediately on left*

* £13-£25 £13-£25 £13-£25

Open all year (rs 10 Sep-20 May Swimming pool closed) Last arrival 22.00hrs Last departure noon

This small family run park is set at the foot of the Quantock Hills and makes an ideal base for touring Somerset, Exmoor and North Devon. It is close to the West Somerset Railway. It has excellent facilities and there is a heated outdoor swimming pool plus a gym and fitness centre. Bike hire is also available. A 3.5 acre site with 69 touring pitches, 30 hardstandings and 8 statics.

Leisure:

Facilities:

Services:

Within 3 miles:

Notes: Off-licence on site

GLASTONBURY

►►►► 76% Isle of Avalon Touring Caravan Park

Godney Rd BA6 9AF

☎ 01458 833618 01458 833618

dir: *M5 junct 23, A39 to outskirts of Glastonbury, 2nd exit signed Wells at B&Q rdbt, straight over next rdbt, 1st exit at 3rd rdbt (B3151), site 200yds right*

Open all year Last arrival 21.00hrs Last departure 11.00hrs

A popular site on the south side of this historic town and within easy walking distance of the town centre. This level park offers a quiet environment in which to stay and explore the many local attractions including the Tor, Wells, Wookey Hole and Clarks Village. An 8 acre site with 120 touring pitches, 70 hardstandings.

Leisure:

Facilities:

Services:

Within 3 miles:

Notes: Cycle hire

MARTOCK

►►►► 82% Southfork Caravan Park

Parrett Works TA12 6AE

☎ 01935 825661 01935 825122

e-mail: southforkcaravans@btconnect.com

dir: *8m NW of Yeovil, 2m off A303. From E, take exit after Cartgate rdbt. From W, 1st exit off rdbt signed South Petherton, follow camping signs*

Open Mar-Oct Last arrival 22.30hrs Last departure noon

A neat grass park in a quiet rural area, offering spotless facilities to those who enjoy the countryside. The park also has a fully-approved caravan repair and servicing centre with accessory shop. Located on the outskirts of a pretty village, with good amenities. A 2 acre site with 27 touring pitches, 2 hardstandings and 3 statics.

Leisure:

Facilities:

Services:

Within 3 miles:

Notes: Wi-fi

PORLOCK

►►►► 82% Burrowhayes Farm Caravan & Camping Site

West Luccombe TA24 8HT

☎ 01643 862463

e-mail: info@burrowhayes.co.uk

dir: *A39 from Minehead towards Porlock for 5m. Left at Red Post to Horner & West Luccombe, site 0.25m on right, immediately before humpback bridge*

* £10-£16.50 £10-£16.50 £10-£16.50

Open 15 Mar-Oct (rs Sat before Etr shop closed) Last arrival 22.00hrs Last departure noon

A delightful site on the edge of Exmoor, sloping gently down to Horner Water. The farm buildings have been converted into riding stables, which offers escorted rides on the moors, and the excellent toilet facilities are housed in timber-clad buildings. There are many walks directly into the countryside. An 8 acre site with 120 touring pitches, 4 hardstandings and 20 statics.

Facilities:

Services:

Within 3 miles:

Notes: Riding stables

SHEPTON MALLET

►► 93% Greenacres Camping

Barrow Ln, North Wootton BA4 4HL

☎ 01749 890497

e-mail: bookings@greenacres-camping.co.uk

dir: *A361 to Glastonbury. Turn at Steanbow Farm, from A39 turn at Brownes Garden Centre. Follow campsite signs & sign for North Wootton*

* fr £14 fr £14

Open Apr-Sep Last arrival 21.00hrs Last departure 11.00hrs

An immaculately maintained site peacefully set within sight of Glastonbury Tor. Mainly family orientated with many thoughtful extra facilities provided, and there is plenty of space for children to play games in a very safe environment. A 4.5 acre site with 40 touring pitches.

Leisure:

Facilities:

Services:

Within 3 miles:

Notes: No caravans or large motorhomes, no pets, no open fires, no BBQs on grass areas. Wi-fi

WATCHET

►►► 85% Home Farm Holiday Centre

St Audries Bay TA4 4DP

☎ 01984 632487 01984 634687

e-mail: dib@homefarmholidaycentre.co.uk

dir: *Follow A39 towards Minehead, right onto B3191 at West Quantoxhead after St Audries garage, then right in 0.25m*

£10-£25 £10-£25 £10-£25

Open all year (rs mid Nov-Etr shop & bar closed) Last arrival dusk Last departure noon

In a hidden valley beneath the Quantock Hills, this park overlooks its own private beach. The atmosphere is friendly and quiet, and there are lovely sea views from the level pitches. Flower beds, woodland walks, and a koi carp pond all enhance this very attractive site, along with a lovely indoor swimming pool and a beer garden. A 45 acre site with 40 touring pitches, 35 hardstandings and 230 statics.

Leisure:

Facilities:

Services:

Within 3 miles:

Notes: No cars by caravans or tents

WELLINGTON

►►► 77% Gamlins Farm Caravan Park

Gamlins Farm House, Greenham TA21 0LZ

☎ 01823 672859 & 07967 683738

01823 673391

e-mail: stephowe@hotmail.co.uk

dir: *M5 junct 26, A38 towards Tiverton & Exeter. 5m, right for Greenham, site 1m on right*

* £8-£12 £8-£12 £6-£12

Open Etr-Oct Last arrival 20.00hrs

A well-planned site in a secluded position with panoramic views. The friendly owners keep the toilet facilities to a good standard of cleanliness. A 3 acre site with 25 touring pitches, 6 hardstandings and 3 statics.

Leisure:

Facilities:

Services:

Within 3 miles:

Notes: Dogs must be kept on leads, no loud noise after 22.00hrs. Free coarse fishing on site

WESTON-SUPER-MARE

►►► 81% West End Farm Caravan & Camping Park

Locking BS24 8RH

☎ 01934 822529 01934 822529

e-mail: robin@westendfarm.org

dir: *M5 junct 21 onto A370. Follow International Helicopter Museum signs. Right at rdbt, follow signs to site*

Open all year Last arrival 18.00hrs Last departure noon

A delightful park bordered by hedges, with good landscaping and well-kept facilities. It is handily located next to a helicopter museum, and offers good access to Weston-Super-Mare and the Mendips. A 10 acre site with 75 touring pitches and 20 statics.

Leisure:

Facilities:

Services:

Within 3 miles:

Notes:

WESTON-SUPER-MARE

►►► 80% Country View Holiday Park

Sand Rd, Sand Bay BS22 9UJ

☎ 01934 627595

e-mail: info@cvhp.co.uk

dir: *M5 junct 21, A370 towards Weston-Super-Mare. Immediately into left lane, follow Kewstoke/Sand Bay signs. Straight over 3 rdbts onto Lower Norton Ln. At Sand Bay right into Sand Rd, site on right*

* £12-£22 £12-£22 £12-£22

Open Mar-Jan Last arrival 20.00hrs Last departure noon

A pleasant open site in a rural area a few hundred yards from Sandy Bay and the beach. The park is also well placed for energetic walks along the coast at either end of the beach. The facilities are excellent and well maintained. 80 seasonal touring pitches are available. An 8 acre site with 120 touring pitches, 90 hardstandings and 65 statics.

Leisure:

Facilities:

Services:

Within 3 miles:

WINSFORD

►►► 77% Halse Farm Caravan & Camping Park

TA24 7JL

☎ 01643 851259 01643 851592

e-mail: enquiries@halsefarm.co.uk

web: www.halsefarm.co.uk

dir: *Signed from A396 at Bridgetown. In Winsford turn left and bear left past pub. 1m up hill, entrance on left immediately after cattle grid*

* £12-£16 £12-£16 £12-£16

Open 22 Mar-Oct Last arrival 22.00hrs Last departure noon

A peaceful little site on Exmoor overlooking a wooded valley with glorious views. This moorland site is quite remote, but it provides good modern toilet facilities which are kept immaculately clean. A good base for exploring the Exmoor National Park. A 3 acre site with 44 touring pitches, 11 hardstandings.

Leisure:

Facilities:

Services:

Within 3 miles:

LEEK

►►► 82% Leek Camping & Caravanning Club Site

Blackshaw Grange, Blackshaw Moor ST13 8TL

☎ 01538 300285

dir: *2m from Leek on A53 (Leek to Buxton road). Site 200yds past Blackshaw Moor sign on left*

Open all year Last arrival 21.00hrs Last departure noon

A beautifully located club site with well-screened pitches. The very good facilities are kept in pristine condition, and children will enjoy the enclosed play area. A 6 acre site with 70 touring pitches, 39 hardstandings.

Leisure:

Facilities:

Services:

Within 3 miles:

Notes: Site gates closed 23.00hrs-07.00hrs

OAKAMOOR

►►►► 80% The Star Caravan & Camping Park

Star Rd, Cotton ST10 3DW

☎ 01538 702219

dir: *From N: M1 junct 28, (or from S: M1 junct 23a) follow Alton Towers signs. With Alton Towers main gate on right, follow for 0.75m to x-rds in Cotton. Take B5417, past Ye Old Star Inn, to site*

* £15-£18 £10-£20 £10-£24

Open Mar-Nov Last arrival 21.00hrs Last departure 11.00hrs

With its close proximity to Alton Towers, this park is a favourite with families visiting the popular attraction. Grounds and buildings are beautifully designed and maintained, and there is an excellent children's playground as well as a football field for working off steam. 65 seasonal touring pitches are available. A 48 acre site with 120 touring pitches, 30 hardstandings and 65 statics.

Leisure:

Facilities:

Services:

Within 3 miles:

Notes: Families & couples only. 5-acre dog walk & wildlife meadow. Wi-fi

IPSWICH

►►► 77% Low House Touring Caravan Centre

Bucklesham Rd, Foxhall IP10 0AU

☎ 01473 659437 & 07710 378029

01473 659880

e-mail: low.house@btinternet.com

dir: *From A14 (south ring road) take slip road to A1156 signed East Ipswich. Right in 1m, right again in 0.5m. Site on left*

fr £14 fr £14 fr £20

Open all year Last arrival anytime Last departure 14.00hrs

A secluded site surrounded by hundreds of mature trees. Buildings have been hand-crafted by the owner in stained timber, and there is a children's play area, and a collection of caged rabbits, bantams and guinea fowl. Tents accepted only if space available. A 3.5 acre site with 30 touring pitches.

Leisure:

Facilities:

Services:

Within 3 miles:

Notes: Dogs must be kept on leads

KESSINGLAND

65% Kessingland Beach Holiday Park

Beach Rd NR33 7RN

☎ 01502 740636 01502 740907

e-mail: holidaysales.kessinglandbeach@park-resorts.com

dir: *From Lowestoft take A12 S. At Kessingland take 3rd exit at rdbt towards beach. Through village. At beach follow road to right. In 400yds fork left for park*

Open Etr-2 Nov Last arrival mdnt Last departure 10.00hrs

A large holiday centre with direct access onto the beach, and a variety of leisure facilities. The touring area is tucked away from the statics, and served by a clean and functional toilet block. A fish and chip shop and Boat House Restaurant are popular features. Seasonal touring pitches available. A 69 acre site with 90 touring pitches and 95 statics.

Leisure:

Facilities:

Services:

Within 3 miles:

Notes: Kids' clubs, entertainment, mini ten-pin bowling

KESSINGLAND

►►►► 86% Heathland Beach Caravan Park

London Rd NR33 7PJ

☎ 01502 740337 01502 742355

e-mail: heathlandbeach@btinternet.com

web: www.heathlandbeach.co.uk

dir: *1m N of Kessingland off A12 onto B1437*

Open Apr-Oct Last arrival 21.00hrs Last departure 11.00hrs

A well-run and maintained park offering superb toilet facilities. The park is set in meadowland, with level grass pitches, and mature trees and bushes. There is direct access to the sea and beach, and good provisions for families on site with a heated swimming pool and three play areas. A 5 acre site with 63 touring pitches and 200 statics.

Leisure:

Facilities:

Services:

Within 3 miles:

Notes: One dog only per unit. Freshwater & sea fishing. Wi-fi

KESSINGLAND

►►►► 84% Kessingland Camping & Caravanning Club Site

Suffolk Wildlife Park, Whites Ln NR33 7TF

☎ 01502 742040

dir: *On A12 from Lowestoft at Kessingland rdbt, follow Wildlife Park signs, turn right to park*

Open 2 Apr-2 Nov Last arrival 21.00hrs Last departure noon

A well screened open site next to Suffolk Wildlife Park, where concessions are available for visitors. An extensive renovation has created superb facilities, including three family rooms, a disabled unit, and smart reception. A well-equipped laundry and covered dishwashing sinks add to the quality amenities. A 5 acre site with 90 touring pitches.

Leisure:

Facilities:

Services:

Within 3 miles:

Notes: Site gates closed 23.00hrs-07.00hrs. Play equipment

WOODBRIDGE

►►►►► 92% Moon & Sixpence

Newbourn Rd, Waldringfield IP12 4PP

☎ 01473 736650 🖷 01473 736270

e-mail: info@moonandsixpence.eu

web: www.moonandsixpence.eu

dir: *Follow caravan & Moon & Sixpence signs from A12 Ipswich (east bypass). 1.5m, left at x-roads*

£18-£30 £18-£30 £18-£30

Open Apr-Oct (rs Low season club, shop, reception open limited hours) Last arrival 20.00hrs Last departure noon

A well-planned site, with tourers occupying a sheltered valley position around a boating lake. Toilet facilities are in a Norwegian cabin, and there is a laundry and dishwashing area. Leisure facilities include tennis courts, a bowling green, fishing, boating and a games room. There is an adult-only area, so no groups, and no noise after 9pm. A 5 acre site with 65 touring pitches and 225 statics.

Leisure: **Facilities:** **Services:** **Within 3 miles:** **Notes:** No group bookings/commercial vehicles, quiet 21.00hrs-08.00hrs. Lake, cycle trail, 10-acre sports area, 9-hole golf. Wi-fi

CHERTSEY

►►►► 83% Chertsey Camping & Caravanning Club Site

Bridge Rd KT16 8JX

☎ 01932 562405

dir: *M25 junct 11, A317 to Chertsey. At rdbt take 1st exit to lights. Straight over at next lights. Right in 400yds, left into site*

Open all year Last arrival 21.00hrs Last departure noon

A pretty Thames-side site set amongst trees and shrubs in well-tended grounds, ideally placed for the M3/M25 and for visiting London. Some attractive riverside pitches are very popular, and fishing and boating is allowed from the site on the river. The toilet facilities are very good. A 12 acre site with 200 touring pitches, 50 hardstandings.

Leisure:

Facilities:

Services:

Within 3 miles:

Notes: Site gates closed 23.00hrs-07.00hrs

EAST HORSLEY

►►► 80% Horsley Camping & Caravanning Club Site

Ockham Road North KT24 6PE

☎ 01483 283273

dir: *From M25 junct 10, A3 towards Guidlford. At 1st major junct follow Ockham/Southend/ Ripley signs. Left, site 2.5m on right. From S: take A3 past Guildford then B2215 towards Ripley*

Open 2 Apr-2 Nov Last arrival 21.00hrs Last departure noon

A beautiful lakeside site with plenty of trees and shrubs and separate camping fields, providing a tranquil base within easy reach of London. Toilet facilities are well maintained and clean. A 9.5 acre site with 130 touring pitches, 41 hardstandings.

Leisure:

Facilities:

Services:

Within 3 miles:

Notes: Site gates closed 23.00hrs-07.00hrs. Fishing

BATTLE

►►► 70% Senlac Wood Holiday Park

Catsfield Rd, Catsfield TN33 9LN

☎ 01424 773969

e-mail: senlacwood@xlninternet.co.uk

dir: *From Battle take A271, left on B2204 signed Bexhill. Site on left*

£13-£15 £13-£15 £13-£15

Open Mar-Oct Last arrival 22.00hrs Last departure noon

An improving woodland site with many secluded bays with hardstanding pitches, and a peaceful grassy glade for tents. The functional toilet facilities are clean, and the site is ideal for anyone looking for seclusion and shade. A 20 acre site with 35 touring pitches, 16 hardstandings.

Leisure:

Facilities:

Services:

Within 3 miles:

Notes: No camp fires

CAMBER

66% Camber Sands

New Lydd Rd TN31 7RT

☎ 0871 664 9719

e-mail: camber.sands@park-resorts.com

dir: *M20 junct 10 (Ashford International Station), A2070 signed Brenzett. Follow Hastings & Rye signs on A259. 1m before Rye, left signed Camber. Site in 3m*

Open Mar-Oct Last arrival anytime Last departure 10.00hrs

Located opposite Camber's vast sandy beach, this large holiday centre offers a good range of leisure and entertainment facilities. The touring area is positioned close to the reception and entrance, and is served by a clean and functional toilet block. 40 touring pitches and 921 statics.

Leisure:

Facilities:

Services:

Within 3 miles:

Notes: Quiet between 23.00hrs-7.00hrs

CROWBOROUGH

►►► 79% Crowborough Camping & Caravanning Club Site

Goldsmith Recreation Ground TN6 2TN

☎ 01892 664827

dir: *Exit A26 into entrance to 'Goldsmiths Ground', signed Leisure Centre. At top of road right onto site lane*

Open 2 Apr-2 Nov Last arrival 21.00hrs Last departure noon

A spacious terraced site with stunning views across the Weald to the North Downs in Kent. This good quality site has clean, modern toilets, a kitchen and eating area for campers, a recreation room, and good provision of hardstandings. An excellent leisure centre is adjacent to the park. A 13 acre site with 90 touring pitches, 26 hardstandings.

Leisure:

Facilities:

Services:

Within 3 miles:

Notes: Site gates closed 23.00hrs-07.00hrs

NORMAN'S BAY

►►► 77% Norman's Bay Camping & Caravanning Club Site

BN24 6PR

☎ 01323 761190

dir: *From rdbt junct of A27/A259 follow A259 signed Eastbourne. In Pevensey Bay village take 1st left signed Beachlands only. 1.25m site on left*

Open 2 Apr-2 Nov Last arrival 20.00hrs Last departure noon

A well kept site with immaculate toilet block, right beside the sea. This popular family park enjoys good rural views towards Rye and Pevensey. A 13 acre site with 200 touring pitches, 5 hardstandings.

Leisure:

Facilities:

Services:

Within 3 miles:

Notes: Site gates closed 23.00hrs-07.00hrs

PEVENSEY BAY

►►► 80% Bay View Park

Old Martello Rd BN24 6DX

☎ 01323 768688 01323 769637

e-mail: holidays@bay-view.co.uk

web: www.bay-view.co.uk

dir: *Signed from A259 W of Pevensey Bay. On sea side of A259 along private road towards beach*

* £14.50-£21 £14.50-£21 £14.50-£21

Open Mar-Oct Last arrival 20.00hrs Last departure noon

A pleasant well-run site just yards from the beach, in an area east of Eastbourne town centre known as 'The Crumbles'. The level grassy site is very well maintained and the new toilet facilities feature fully-serviced cubicles. A 6 acre site with 94 touring pitches, 10 hardstandings and 8 statics.

Leisure:

Facilities:

Services:

Within 3 miles:

Notes: Families & couples only. No commercial vehicles. 9-hole golf course. Wi-fi

CHICHESTER

►►► 79% Ellscott Park

Sidlesham Ln, Birdham PO20 7QL

☎ 01243 512003 📠 01243 512003

e-mail: camping@ellscottpark.co.uk

dir: *Take A286 (Chichester/Wittering road) for approx 4m, left at Butterfly Farm sign, site 500yds right*

£12-£18 £12-£18 £12-£16

Open Apr-3rd wk in Oct Last arrival daylight Last departure variable

A well-kept park set in meadowland behind the owners' nursery and van storage area. The park attracts a peace-loving clientele, and is handy for the beach and other local attractions. Home-grown produce and eggs are for sale. A 2.5 acre site with 50 touring pitches.

Leisure:

Facilities:

Services:

Within 3 miles:

Notes:

DIAL POST

►►►► 86% Honeybridge Park

Honeybridge Ln RH13 8NX

☎ 01403 710923 📠 01403 710923

e-mail: enquiries@honeybridgepark.co.uk

dir: *10m S of Horsham, just off A24 at Dial Post. Behind Old Barn Nursery*

Open all year Last arrival 21.00hrs Last departure noon

An attractive and very popular park on gently-sloping ground surrounded by hedgerows and mature trees. A comprehensive amenities building houses upmarket toilet facilities including luxury family and disabled rooms, as well as a laundry, shop and off-licence. There are plenty of hardstandings and electric hook-ups, and an excellent children's play area. 25 seasonal touring pitches available. A 15 acre site with 180 touring pitches, 75 hardstandings and 20 statics.

Leisure:

Facilities:

Services:

Within 3 miles:

Notes: Dogs must be kept on leads, no open fires. Fridges

SELSEY

79% Warner Farm Touring Park

Warner Ln, Selsey PO20 9EL

☎ 01243 604499

e-mail: touring@bunnleisure.co.uk

web: www.warnerfarm.co.uk

dir: *From B2145 in Selsey turn right onto School Lane & follow signs*

Open Mar-Oct Last arrival 17.30hrs Last departure 10.00hrs

A well-screened touring site with newly refurbished toilet facilities that adjoins the three static parks under the same ownership. A courtesy bus runs around the complex to entertainment areas and supermarkets. The park backs onto open grassland, and the leisure facilities with bar, amusements and bowling alley, and swimming pool/sauna complex are also accessible to tourers. A 10 acre site with 250 touring pitches, 60 hardstandings and 1500 statics.

Leisure:

Facilities:

Services:

Within 3 miles:

SOUTH SHIELDS

►►► 69% Lizard Lane Caravan & Camping Site

Lizard Ln NE34 7AB

☎ 0191 454 4982 & 455 7411

0191 427 0469

dir: *2m S of town centre on A183 (Sunderland road)*

Open Mar-Oct Last arrival anytime Last departure 11.00hrs

A well-kept site on sloping ground near the beach, not far from the city of Sunderland with its many attractions. A 2 acre site with 45 touring pitches and 70 statics.

Leisure:

Facilities:

Services:

Within 3 miles:

Notes: 9-hole putting green

KINGSBURY

►►►► 86% Kingsbury Water Park Camping & Caravanning Club Site

Kingsbury Water Park, Bodymoor, Heath Ln B76 0DY

☎ 01827 874101

dir: *M42 junct 9, B4097 (Kingsbury road). Left at rdbt, past main entrance to water park, over motorway, take next right. Follow lane for 0.5m to site*

Open all year Last arrival 21.00hrs Last departure noon

A very upmarket site providing high standards in every area. Along with private washing facilities in the quality toilets, there is good security on this attractive former gravel pit, with its complex of lakes, canals, woods and marshland, with good access roads. A n18 acre site with 150 touring pitches, 75 hardstandings.

Leisure:

Facilities:

Services:

Within 3 miles:

Notes: Site gates closed 23.00hrs-07.00hrs

WOLVEY

►►► 75% Wolvey Villa Farm Caravan & Camping Site

LE10 3HF

☎ 01455 220493 & 220630

dir: *M6 junct 2, B4065 follow Wolvey signs. Or M69 junct 1 & follow Wolvey signs*

£13-£14 £13-£14 £10-£11

Open all year Last arrival 22.00hrs Last departure noon

A level grass site surrounded by trees and shrubs, on the borders of Warwickshire and Leicestershire. This quiet country site has its own popular fishing lake, and is convenient for visiting the major cities of Coventry and Leicester. A 7 acre site with 110 touring pitches, 24 hardstandings.

Leisure:

Facilities:

Services:

Within 3 miles:

Notes: No twin axles. Putting green, off licence

COWES

84% Thorness Bay Holiday Park

Thorness PO31 8NJ

☎ 01983 523109 📠 01983 822213

e-mail: holidaysales.thornessbay@park-resorts.com

dir: *On A3054 towards Yarmouth, 1st right after BMW garage, signed Thorness Bay*

Open Mar-1 Nov Last arrival anytime Last departure 10.00hrs

Splendid views of The Solent can be enjoyed from this rural park located just outside Cowes. A footpath leads directly to the coast, while on site there is an all-weather sports court, entertainment clubs for children, and cabaret, shows and a bar for all the family. There are 23 serviced pitches with TV boosters. A 148 acre site with 80 touring pitches, 20 hardstandings and 560 statics.

Leisure:

Facilities:

Services:

Within 3 miles:

Notes: Evening entertainment, water slide

NEWBRIDGE

►►►►► 91% Orchards Holiday Caravan Park

Main Rd PO41 0TS

☎ 01983 531331 & 531350

📠 01983 531666

e-mail: info@orchards-holiday-park.co.uk

web: www.orchards-holiday-park.co.uk

dir: *4m E of Yarmouth; 6m W of Newport on B3401. Take A3054 from Yarmouth, after 3m turn right at Horse & Groom Inn. Follow signs to Newbridge. Entrance opposite Post Office*

Open 11 Feb-2 Jan (rs Mar-Oct takeaway, shop, outdoor pool open) Last arrival 23.00hrs Last departure 11.00hrs

Peaceful village location amid downs and meadowland. Pitches are terraced, and offer a good provision of hardstandings, including super pitches. Excellent facilities, alongside disabled access to all facilities, plus disabled toilets. A 15 acre site with 171 touring pitches, 74 hardstandings and 65 statics.

Leisure: **Facilities:** **Services:** **Within 3 miles:** **Notes:** Petanque, table tennis room, poolside café

PONDWELL

►►► 76% Pondwell Camp Site

PO34 5AQ

☎ 01983 612330 01983 613511

dir: *From Ryde take A3055 then left on B3330 to Seaview. Site next to Wishing Well pub*

Open May-26 Sep Last arrival 23.00hrs Last departure 11.00hrs

A secluded site in quiet rural surroundings close to the sea, on slightly sloping ground with some level areas. The village is within easy walking distance. A 9 acre site with 150 touring pitches.

Leisure:

Facilities:

Services:

Within 3 miles:

Notes: No pets, no unaccompanied children

RYDE

►►►►► 85% Whitefield Forest Touring Park

Brading Rd PO33 1QL

☎ 01983 617069

e-mail: pat&louise@whitefieldforest.co.uk

web: www.whitefieldforest.co.uk

dir: *From Ryde follow A3055 towards Brading, after Tesco rdbt site 0.5m on left*

£11.50-£17 £11.50-£17 £11.50-£17

Open Etr-Oct Last arrival 21.00hrs Last departure 11.00hrs

This park is beautifully laid out in Whitefield Forest, and offers a wide variety of pitches, all of which have electricity. It offers excellent modern facilities which are spotlessly clean. The park takes great care in retaining the natural beauty of the forest, and is a haven for wildlife, including the red squirrel. A 23 acre site with 80 touring pitches, 20 hardstandings.

Leisure:

Facilities:

Services:

Within 3 miles:

Notes: Wi-fi

ST HELENS

85% Nodes Point Holiday Park

Nodes Rd PO33 1YA

☎ 01983 872401 01983 874696

e-mail: gm.nodespoint@park-resorts.com

dir: *From Ryde take B3330 signed Seaview/ Puckpool. At junct for Puckpool bear right. 1m past Road Side Inn in Nettlestone, site on left*

Open Mar-Oct Last arrival 21.00hrs Last departure 10.00hrs

A well-equipped holiday centre on an elevated position overlooking Bembridge Bay with direct access to the beach. The touring area is mostly sloping with some terraces. Activities are organised for youngsters, and there is entertainment for the whole family. Buses pass the main entrance. A 16 acre site with 145 touring pitches and 195 statics.

Leisure:

Facilities:

Services:

Within 3 miles:

Notes: Family park

SANDOWN

►►►► 78% Old Barn Touring Park

Cheverton Farm, Newport Rd, Apse Heath PO36 9PJ

☎ 01983 866414 01983 865988

e-mail: oldbarn@weltinet.com

dir: *On A3056 from Newport, site on left after Apse Heath rdbt*

* £13.50-£17 £13.50-£17 £13.50-£17

Open May-Sep Last arrival 21.00hrs Last departure noon

A terraced site with good quality facilities, bordering on open farmland. The spacious pitches are secluded and fully serviced, and there is a decent modern toilet block. A 5 acre site with 60 touring pitches, 9 hardstandings.

Leisure:

Facilities:

Services:

Within 3 miles:

SANDOWN

►►►► 77% Adgestone Camping & Caravanning Club Site

Lower Adgestone Rd PO36 0HL

☎ 01983 403432

dir: *Exit A3055 (Sandown/Shanklin road) at Manor House pub, in Lake. Past school & golf course on left, right at T-junct, site 200yds on right*

Open 2 Apr-2 Nov Last arrival 21.00hrs Last departure noon

A popular, well-managed park in a quiet, rural location not far from Sandown. The level pitches are imaginatively laid out, and surrounded by beautiful flower beds and trees set close to a small river. This planting offers good screening as well as enhancing the appearance of the park. There is excellent provision for families in general. A 22 acre site with 270 touring pitches.

Leisure:

Facilities:

Services:

Within 3 miles:

Notes: Site gates closed 23.00hrs-07.00hrs. Fishing

SHANKLIN

83% Lower Hyde Holiday Park

Landguard Rd PO37 7LL

☎ 01983 866131 01983 862532

e-mail: holidaysales.lowerhyde@park-resorts.com

dir: *From Fishbourne ferry terminal follow A3055 to Shanklin. Site signed just past lake*

Open Mar-1 Nov Last arrival anytime Last departure 10.00hrs

A popular holiday park on the outskirts of Shanklin, close to the sandy beaches. There is an outdoor swimming pool and plenty of organised activities for youngsters of all ages. In the evening there is a choice of family entertainment. The touring facilities are located in a quiet area away from the main complex, with good views over the downs. A 65 acre site with 82 touring pitches and 313 statics.

Leisure:

Facilities:

Services:

Within 3 miles:

Notes: No cars by caravans. Water flume, evening entertainment, kids' club

SHANKLIN

►►► 79%
Ninham Country Holidays

Ninham PO37 7PL

☎ 01983 864243 & 866040
01983 868881

e-mail: office@ninham-holidays.co.uk

dir: *Signed off A3056 (Newport to Sandown road)*

Open May day BH-15 Sep (rs end May-early Sep outdoor pool heated)

Enjoying a lofty rural position with fine country views, this delightful, spacious park occupies two separate, well-maintained areas in a country park setting near the sea and beach. A 12 acre site with 98 touring pitches, 4 hardstandings.

Leisure:
Facilities:
Services:
Within 3 miles:
Notes: Swimming pool & coarse fishing rules apply. Dish wash areas, all-service pitches. Wi-fi

WHITECLIFF BAY

82% Whitecliff Bay Holiday Park

Hillway Rd, Bembridge PO35 5PL

☎ 01983 872671 01983 872941

e-mail: holiday@whitecliff-bay.com

dir: *1m S of Bembridge, signed off B3395 in village*

* £4-£46 £4-£46 £4-£46

Open Mar-Oct Last arrival 21.00hrs Last departure 10.30hrs

A large seaside complex on two sites, with camping on one and self-catering chalets and statics on the other. There is an indoor pool with flume and spa pool, and an outdoor pool with a kiddies' pool, a family entertainment club, and plenty of traditional on-site activities including crazy golf, a soft play area and table tennis plus a restaurant and a choice of bars. There is easy access to a lovely sandy beach. 50 seasonal touring pitches. A 49 acre site with 400 touring pitches, 50 hardstandings and 227 statics.

Leisure:
Facilities:
Services:
Within 3 miles:
Notes: Adults & families only

DEVIZES

►►►► 84% Devizes Camping & Caravanning Club Site

Spout Ln, Nr Seend, Melksham SN12 6RN

☎ 01380 828839

dir: *From Devizes on A361 right onto A365, over canal, next left into lane beside Three Magpies pub. Site on right*

Open all year Last arrival 21.00hrs Last departure noon

An excellent club site with well designed, quality facilities and a high level of staff commitment. This popular park is set beside the Kennet and Avon Canal, with a gate to the towpath for walking and cycling, and with fishing available in the canal. Well situated for exploring Salisbury Plain and the Marlborough Downs. A 13.5 acre site with 90 touring pitches, 70 hardstandings.

Leisure:

Facilities:

Services:

Within 3 miles:

Notes: Site gates closed 23.00hrs-07.00hrs

SALISBURY

►►►► 82% Coombe Touring Park

Race Plain, Netherhampton SP2 8PN

☎ 01722 328451 01722 328451

e-mail: enquiries@coombecaravanpark.co.uk

dir: *Exit A36 onto A3094, 2m SW, site adjacent to Salisbury racecourse*

* £11-£14 £11-£14 £11-£14

Open 3 Jan-20 Dec (rs Oct-May shop closed) Last arrival 21.00hrs Last departure noon

A very neat and attractive site adjacent to the racecourse with views over the downs. The park is well landscaped with shrubs and maturing trees, and the very colourful beds are stocked from the owner's greenhouse. A comfortable park with a superb luxury toilet block, and four static holiday homes for hire. A 3 acre site with 50 touring pitches and 4 statics.

Facilities:

Services:

Within 3 miles:

Notes: No disposable BBQs or fires, no mini motorbikes. Children's bathroom

WESTBURY

►►►► 79% Brokerswood Country Park

Brokerswood BA13 4EH

☎ 01373 822238 🖷 01373 858474

e-mail: info@brokerswood.co.uk

web: www.brokerswood.co.uk

dir: *M4 junct 17, S on A350. Right at Yarnbrook to Rising Sun pub at North Bradley, left at rdbt. Left on bend approaching Southwick, 2.5m, site on right*

* £10-£28 £10-£28 £10-£28

Open all year Last arrival 21.30hrs Last departure 11.00hrs

A popular park on the edge of an 80-acre woodland park with nature trails and fishing lakes. An adventure playground offers plenty of fun for all ages, and there is a miniature railway, an indoor play centre, and a café. There are high quality toilet facilities and fully-equipped, ready-erected tents are now available for hire. A 5 acre site with 69 touring pitches, 21 hardstandings.

Leisure:

Facilities:

Services:

Within 3 miles:

Notes: Families only

HANLEY SWAN

►►►► 80% Blackmore Camping & Caravanning Club Site

Blackmore Camp Site No 2 WR8 0EE

☎ 01684 310280

dir: *A38 to Upton on Severn. Turn N over river bridge. 2nd left, 1st left signed Hanley Swan. Site 1m on right*

Open all year Last arrival 21.00hrs Last departure noon

Blackmore is a well-established, level wooded park, ideally located for exploring the Malvern Hills and Worcester. The excellent toilet facilities are spotlessly maintained. A 17 acre site with 200 touring pitches, 66 hardstandings.

Leisure:

Facilities:

Services:

Within 3 miles:

Notes: Site gates closed 23.00hrs-07.00hrs

HONEYBOURNE

►►►► 84% Ranch Caravan Park

Station Rd WR11 7PR

☎ 01386 830744 01386 833503

e-mail: enquiries@ranch.co.uk

dir: *Through village x-rds towards Bidford, site 400mtrs on left*

* £19-£24 £19-£24

Open Mar-Nov (rs Mar-May & Sep-Nov swimming pool closed, shorter club hours) Last arrival 20.00hrs Last departure noon

An attractive and well-run park set amidst farmland in the Vale of Evesham and landscaped with trees and bushes. Tourers have their own excellent facilities in two locations, and the use of an outdoor heated swimming pool in peak season. There is also a licensed club serving meals. A 12 acre site with 120 touring pitches, 43 hardstandings and 218 statics.

Leisure:

Facilities:

Services:

Within 3 miles:

Notes: No tents. No unaccompanied minors. Gym & sauna (chargeable)

ROMSLEY

►►►► 78% Clent Hills Camping & Caravanning Club Site

Fieldhouse Ln B62 0NH

☎ 01562 710015

dir: *M5 junct 3, A456. Left on B4551 to Romsley. Right past Sun Hotel, 5th left, next left. Site 330yds on left*

Open 2 Apr-2 Nov Last arrival 21.00hrs Last departure noon

A very pretty, well tended park surrounded by wooded hills. The site offers excellent facilities, including hardstandings to provide flat pitches for motorhomes. Lovely views of the Clent Hills can be enjoyed from this park, and there are plenty of local scenic walks. A 7.5 acre site with 95 touring pitches, 27 hardstandings.

Leisure:

Facilities:

Services:

Within 3 miles:

Notes: Site gates closed 23.00hrs-07.00hrs

WOLVERLEY

►►► 79% Wolverley Camping & Caravanning Club Site

Brown Westhead Park DY10 3PX

☎ 01562 850909

dir: *From Kidderminster A449 to Wolverhampton, left at lights onto B4189 signed Wolverley. Follow brown camping signs, turn right. Site on left*

Open 2 Apr-2 Nov Last arrival 21.00hrs Last departure noon

A very pleasant grassy site on the edge of the village, with the canal lock and towpath close to the entrance, and a pub overlooking the water. The site has good access to and from nearby motorways. A 12 acre site with 120 touring pitches.

Leisure:

Facilities:

Services:

Within 3 miles:

Notes: Site gates closed 23.00hrs-07.00hrs

BRANDESBURTON

►►► 78% Dacre Lakeside Park

YO25 8RT

☎ 0800 1804556 📠 01964 544040

e-mail: dacrepark@btconnect.com

dir: *Off A165 bypass, midway between Beverley & Hornsea*

Open Mar-Oct Last arrival 21.00hrs Last departure noon

A large lake popular with watersports enthusiasts is the focal point of this grassy site. The clubhouse offers indoor activities; there's a fish and chip shop, pub and Chinese takeaway in the village, which is within walking distance. The 6-acre lake is used for windsurfing, sailing, kayaking, canoeing and fishing. A n8 acre site with 120 touring pitches.

Leisure:

Facilities:

Services:

Within 3 miles:

Notes: Bowling

BRIDLINGTON

►►► 80% Fir Tree Caravan Park

Jewison Ln, Sewerby YO16 6YG

☎ 01262 676442 01262 608242

e-mail: info@flowerofmay.com

dir: *1.5m from centre of Bridlington. Turn left off B1255 at Marton Corner. Site 600yds on left*

Open Mar-Oct (rs Early & late season bar & entertainment restrictions) Last arrival 21.00hrs Last departure noon

Fir Tree Park has a well laid out touring area with its own facilities within a large, mainly static park. It has an excellent swimming pool complex, and the adjacent conservatory bar serves meals. There is also a family bar, games room and outdoor children's play area. A 22 acre site with 45 touring pitches, 45 hardstandings and 400 statics.

Leisure:

Facilities:

Services:

Within 3 miles:

Notes: Dogs allowed by arrangement only. Wi-fi

RUDSTON

►►► 79% Thorpe Hall Caravan & Camping Site

Thorpe Hall YO25 4JE

☎ 01262 420393 & 420574

01262 420588

e-mail: caravansite@thorpehall.co.uk

dir: *5m from Bridlington on B1253*

* £14.50-£27.50 £14.50-£27.50 £10.50-£23.50

Open Mar-Oct (rs Limited opening hours reception & shop) Last arrival 22.00hrs Last departure noon

A delightful, peaceful small park within the walled gardens of Thorpe Hall yet within a few miles of the bustling seaside resort of Bridlington. The site offers a games field, its own coarse fishery, pitch & putt, and a games and TV lounge, and there are numerous walks locally. There is a newy refurbished amenity block. A 4.5 acre site with 90 touring pitches.

Leisure:

Facilities:

Services:

Within 3 miles:

Notes: Golf practice area (4.5 acres). Wi-fi

SKIPSEA

84% Low Skirlington Leisure Park

YO25 8SY

☎ 01262 468213 & 468466

01262 468105

e-mail: info@skirlington.com

dir: *From M62 towards Beverley then Hornsea. Between Skipsea & Hornsea on B1242*

Open Mar-Oct

A large well-run seaside park set close to the beach in partly-sloping meadowland with young trees and shrubs. The site has five toilet blocks, a supermarket and an amusement arcade, with occasional entertainment in the clubhouse. The wide range of family amenities include an indoor heated swimming pool complex with sauna, jacuzzi and sunbeds. A 10-pin bowling alley and indoor play area for children are added attractions. A 24 acre site with 285 touring pitches, 15 hardstandings and 450 statics.

Leisure:

Facilities:

Services:

Within 3 miles:

Notes: Putting green

SPROATLEY

►►► 80% Burton Constable Holiday Park & Arboretum

Old Lodges HU11 4LN

☎ 01964 562508 01964 563420

e-mail: info@burtonconstable.co.uk

dir: *Off A165 onto B1238 to Sproatley. Follow signs to site*

* £14.50-£26 £14.50-£26 £14.50-£22

Open Mar-Jan (rs Mar-Oct tourers/tents) Last arrival 22.00hrs Last departure 14.00hrs

A very attractive parkland site overlooking the fishing lakes, in the grounds of Burton Constable Hall. The toilet facilities are kept very clean, and the Lakeside Club provides a focus for relaxing in the evening. Children will enjoy the extensive adventure playground. A 90 acre site with 140 touring pitches, 14 hardstandings and 339 statics.

Leisure:

Facilities:

Services:

Within 3 miles:

Notes: Dogs must be kept on leads. No skateboards or rollerblades. Two 10-acre fishing lakes, snooker table

WITHERNSEA

72% Withernsea Sands

Waxholme Rd HU19 2BS

☎ 0871 664 9803

e-mail: withernsea.sands@park-resorts.com

dir: *M62 junct 38, A63 through Hull. At end of dual carriageway, turn right onto A1033, follow Withernsea signs. Through village, left at mini-rdbt onto B1242. Next right at lighthouse. Site 0.5m on left*

* £5-£25 £5-£25 £5-£25

Open Mar-Oct (rs BH & peak wknds Entertainment & sports available) Last departure 10.00hrs

Touring is very much at the heart of this holiday park's operation, with 100 all electric pitches and additional space for tents. Park Resorts are in the process of upgrading the facilities and attractions, and the leisure complex with its futuristic design is especially impressive. Seasonal touring pitches available. 120 touring pitches and 422 statics.

Leisure: **Facilities:** **Services:**

Within 3 miles:

Notes: Extension leads/utilities from reception

ALLERSTON

►►►► 81% Vale of Pickering Caravan Park

Carr House Farm YO18 7PQ

☎ 01723 859280 01723 850060

e-mail: tony@valeofpickering.co.uk

dir: *On B1415, 1.75m off A170 (Pickering-Scarborough road)*

* £14-£22 £14-£22 £11-£14

Open 5 Mar-3 Jan (rs Mar) Last arrival 21.00hrs Last departure 11.30hrs

A well-maintained, spacious family park with excellent facilities including a well-stocked shop. Younger children will enjoy the attractive play area, while the large ball sports area will attract older ones. The park is set in open countryside bounded by hedges, and is handy for the North Yorkshire Moors and the attractions of Scarborough. A 13 acre site with 120 touring pitches, 80 hardstandings.

Leisure:

Facilities:

Services:

Within 3 miles:

Notes: Microwave

BOROUGHBRIDGE

►►►► 77% Boroughbridge Camping & Caravanning Club Site

Bar Ln, Roecliffe YO51 9LS

☎ 01423 322683

dir: *From A1(M) junct 48 follow signs for Bar Lane Ind Est & Roecliffe. Site 0.25m from rdbt*

Open all year Last arrival 21.00hrs Last departure noon

A quiet riverside site with direct access onto the River Ure, with fishing and boating available. Close enough to the A1(M) but far enough away to hear little traffic noise, this site is a perfect stopover for longer journeys. Ripon, Knaresborough, Harrogate and York are within easy reach, and Boroughbridge offers plenty of facilities just a short walk away. A 5 acre site with 85 touring pitches, 13 hardstandings.

Leisure:

Facilities:

Services:

Within 3 miles:

Notes: Site gates closed 23.00hrs-07.00hrs

FILEY

89% Flower of May Holiday Park

Lebberston Cliff YO11 3NU

☎ 01723 584311 🖷 01723 581361

e-mail: info@flowerofmay.com

dir: *Signed off A165 on Scarborough side of Filey*

* £18-£24 £18-£24 £14-£24

Open Etr-Oct (rs Early & late season restricted opening in cafe, shop & bars) Last arrival 21.00hrs Last departure noon

A well-run, high quality family holiday park with top class facilities. This large landscaped park offers a full range of recreational activities, with plenty for everyone. Grass or hard pitches are available, all on level ground, and arranged in avenues screened by shrubs. 200 seasonal touring pitches available. A 13 acre site with 300 touring pitches, 200 hardstandings and 193 statics.

Leisure:

Facilities:

Services:

Within 3 miles:

Notes: 1 dog per pitch by arrangement only. Squash, bowling, 9-hole golf, basketball court, skate park

FILEY

80% Primrose Valley Holiday Park

YO14 9RF

☎ 01723 513771 & 0870 405 0126

01723 513777

e-mail: lisa.mcewan@bourne-leisure.co.uk

dir: *Signed off A165 (Scarborough-Bridlington road), 3m S of Filey*

* £14-£82 £14-£82

Open mid Mar-Oct Last arrival anytime Last departure 10.00hrs

A large all-action holiday centre with a wide range of sports and leisure activities to suit everyone from morning until late in the evening. The touring area is completely separate from the main park with its own high quality amenity block. All touring pitches are fully-serviced hardstandings with grassed awning strips. A 160 acre site with 50 touring pitches, 50 hardstandings and 1514 statics.

Leisure:

Facilities:

Services:

Within 3 miles:

Notes: Maximum of 2 dogs per group, certain dog breeds banned. Wi-fi

FILEY

74% Reighton Sands Holiday Park

Reighton Gap YO14 9SH

☎ 01723 890476 01723 891043

e-mail: jon.cussins@bourne-leisure.co.uk

dir: *On A165, 5m S of Filey at Reighton Gap, signed*

* £6-£50 £6-£50 £6-£34

Open mid Mar-Oct (rs mid Mar-May & Sep-Oct some facilities may be reduced) Last arrival 22.00hrs Last departure noon

A large, lively holiday centre with a wide range of entertainment and all-weather leisure facilities, located just a 10-minute walk from a long sandy beach. There are good all-weather pitches and a large tenting field. The site is particularly geared towards families with young children. 10 seasonal touring pitches available. A 229 acre site with 83 touring pitches, 83 hardstandings and 800 statics.

Leisure:

Facilities:

Services:

Within 3 miles:

Notes: Indoor play area. Wi-fi

FILEY

73% Blue Dolphin Holiday Park

Gristhorpe Bay YO14 9PU

☎ 01723 515155 01723 512059

dir: *Site off A165, 2m N of Filey*

* £6-£60 £6-£60 £6-£38

Open mid Mar-Oct (rs mid Mar-May & Sep-Oct some facilities may be reduced) Last arrival mdnt Last departure 10.00hrs

There are great clifftop views from this fun-filled holiday centre with an extensive and separate touring area. The emphasis is on non-stop entertainment, with organised sports and clubs, all-weather leisure facilities, heated swimming pools and plenty of well-planned amusements. Pitches are mainly on level or gently-sloping grass plus some fully-serviced hardstandings. The beach is just two miles away. A 85 acre site with 343 touring pitches, 21 hardstandings and 600 statics.

Leisure:

Facilities:

Services:

Within 3 miles:

Notes: Dogs must be kept on leads, maximum of 2 dogs per group, certain dog breeds banned. Multi-sports court, kids' clubs

FILEY

►►► 74% Crows Nest Caravan Park

Gristhorpe YO14 9PS

☎ 01723 582206 01723 582206

e-mail: enquires@crowsnestcaravanpark.com

dir: *5m S of Scarborough & 2m N of Filey. On seaward side of A165, signed off rdbt, near petrol station*

Open Mar-Oct Last departure noon

A beautifully situated park on the coast between Scarborough and Filey, with excellent panoramic views. This large and mainly static park offers lively entertainment, and two bars. The touring caravan area is near the entertainment complex, whilst the tenting pitches are at the top of the site. A 20 acre site with 49 touring pitches, 49 hardstandings and 217 statics.

Leisure:

Facilities:

Services:

Within 3 miles:

Notes: Free entertainment in bar

HARROGATE

►►►►► 80%

Rudding Holiday Park

Follifoot HG3 1JH

☎ 01423 870439 📠 01423 870859

e-mail: holiday-park@ruddingpark.com

web: www.ruddingpark.co.uk

dir: *From A1 take A59 to A658 signed Bradford. 4.5m then right, follow signs*

Open Mar-Jan (rs Nov-Jan shop & Deer House pub - limited opening) Last arrival 22.30hrs Last departure 14.00hrs

A spacious site set in the 200-acre Rudding Park, enhanced with terraced pitches and dry-stone walls. A separate area houses super pitches where services are supplied including TV connection. Toilets are excellent. A golf course, heated outdoor swimming pool, a bar and restaurant, and a play area complete the amenities. A 55 acre site with 141 touring pitches, 60 hardstandings and 95 statics.

Leisure: **Facilities:** **Services:** **Within 3 miles:**

Notes: No under 18s without adult. Driving range, 6-hole short course, golf academy. Wi-fi

HARROGATE

►►►►► 73%

Ripley Caravan Park

Knaresborough Rd, Ripley HG3 3AU

☎ 01423 770050 📠 01423 770050

e-mail: ripleycaravanpark@talk21.com

web: www.ripleycaravanpark.com

dir: *3m N of Harrogate on A61. Right at rdbt onto B6165 signed Knaresborough. Site 300yds left*

* £13.75-£15.75 £13.75-£15.75 £13.75-£15.75

Open Etr-Oct Last arrival 21.00hrs Last departure noon

Well-run rural site in attractive meadowland, landscaped with mature tree plantings. Facilities are well maintained, and there are a heated swimming pool and sauna, games room, and covered play room. An 18 acre site with 100 touring pitches, 35 hardstandings and 50 statics.

Leisure: **Facilities:** **Services:** **Within 3 miles:**

Notes: Family camping only. Dogs must be kept on leads, BBQs must be off the ground. Nursery playroom, football

HARROGATE

►►►► 77% High Moor Farm Park

Skipton Rd HG3 2LT

☎ 01423 563637 & 564955
01423 529449

e-mail: highmoorfarmpark@btconnect.com

dir: *4m W of Harrogate on A59 towards Skipton*

£20-£22 £20-£22

Open Etr or Apr-Oct Last arrival 23.30hrs Last departure 15.00hrs

An excellent site with very good facilities, set beside a small wood and surrounded by thorn hedges. The numerous touring pitches are located in meadowland fields, each area with its own toilet block. A large heated indoor swimming pool, games room, 9-hole golf course, full-sized crown bowling green, and a bar serving meals and snacks are all popular. No tents. 57 seasonal touring pitches available. A 15 acre site with 320 touring pitches, 51 hardstandings and 158 statics.

Leisure:

Facilities:

Services:

Within 3 miles:

Notes: Coarse fishing

HELMSLEY

►►►► 81% Golden Square Touring Caravan Park

Oswaldkirk YO62 5YQ

☎ 01439 788269 01439 788236

e-mail: reception@goldensquarecaravanpark.com

dir: *From Thirsk A19 towards York turn left onto Caravan Route to Helmsley (1m out of Ampleforth village). From York B1363, turn off B1257 to Ampleforth, 0.5m on right*

* £14-£17

Open Mar-Oct Last arrival 21.00hrs Last departure noon

An excellent site with very good facilities, set in a rural situation with views over the North Yorks Moors. Terraced on three levels and surrounded by trees, it is very family-friendly. Country walks and mountain bike trails start here and a new holiday home development is underway. NB: caravans are prohibited from the A170 at Sutton Bank between Thirsk and Helmsley. A 12 acre site with 129 touring pitches, 10 hardstandings and 10 statics.

Leisure: **Facilities:** **Services:** **Within 3 miles:** **Notes:** No skateboards or fires. Microwave

HIGH BENTHAM

►►►► 82%

Riverside Caravan Park

LA2 7FJ

☎ 015242 61272 015242 62835

e-mail: info@riversidecaravanpark.co.uk

dir: *Off B6480, signed from High Bentham town centre*

* £17.50-£22.50 £17.50-£22.50

Open Mar-Nov (rs 28 Dec-2 Jan) Last arrival 20.00hrs Last departure noon

A well-managed riverside park developed to a high standard, with level grass pitches set in avenues separated by trees. It has an excellent, modern amenity block. The games room and adventure playground are popular with families, and the market town of High Bentham is close by. 50 seasonal touring pitches available. A 12 acre site with 61 touring pitches, 27 hardstandings and 206 statics.

Leisure:

Facilities:

Services:

Within 3 miles:

Notes: No tents. Permits for private fishing (chargeable). Wi-fi

HUNMANBY

►►► 79%

Orchard Farm Holiday Village

Stonegate YO14 0PU

☎ 01723 891582 01723 891582

e-mail: sharon.dugdale@virgin.net

dir: *A165 from Scarborough towards Bridlington. Turn right signed Hunmanby, site on right just after rail bridge*

Open Mar-Oct (rs Off peak some facilities restricted) Last arrival 23.00hrs Last departure 11.00hrs

Pitches are arranged around a large coarse fishing lake at this grassy park. The young owners are keen and friendly, and offer a wide range of amenities including an indoor heated swimming pool and a licensed bar. A 14 acre site with 91 touring pitches, 34 hardstandings and 46 statics.

Leisure:

Facilities:

Services:

Within 3 miles:

Notes: Minature railway

NORTHALLERTON

►►►► 78% Otterington Park

Station Farm, South Otterington DL7 9JB

☎ 01609 780656

e-mail: info@otteringtonpark.com

dir: *Turn W off A168 midway between Northallerton & Thirsk, signed South Otterington. Site on right just before South Otterington*

* £15-£19 £15-£19

Open Mar-Oct Last arrival 21.00hrs Last departure 13.00hrs

A high quality park on a working farm with open outlooks across the Vale of York. A peaceful location with a lovely nature walk and on-site fishing which is popular. Young children will enjoy the play area. Toilet facilities are very good. The attractions of Northallerton and Thirsk are a few minutes' drive away. A 5 acre site with 40 touring pitches, 40 hardstandings.

Leisure:

Facilities:

Services:

Within 3 miles:

Notes: Hot tub, fitness equipment. Wi-fi

OSMOTHERLEY

►►►► 78% Cote Ghyll Caravan & Camping Park

DL6 3AH

☎ 01609 883425

e-mail: hills@coteghyll.com

dir: *Exit A19 dual carriageway at A684 (Northallerton junct). Follow signs to Osmotherley. Left in village centre. Site entrance 0.5m on right*

* £14.50-£18.50 £14.50-£18.50 £14.50-£18.50

Open Mar-Oct Last arrival 22.00hrs Last departure noon

A quiet, peaceful site in a pleasant valley on the edge of moors, close to the village. The park is divided into terraces bordered by woodland, and the well-appointed amenity block is a welcome addition to the park. There are pubs and shops nearby and holiday statics for hire. A 7 acre site with 77 touring pitches, 12 hardstandings and 18 statics.

Leisure: **Facilities:** **Services:** **Within 3 miles:** **Notes:** Family park, dogs must be kept on leads at all times. Tourist information, packed lunch service. Wi-fi

PICKERING

►►► 77% Wayside Caravan Park

Wrelton YO18 8PG

01751 472608 01751 472608

e-mail: waysideparks@freenet.co.uk

web: www.waysideparks.co.uk

dir: *2.5m W of Pickering off A170, follow signs at Wrelton*

* £17 £16

Open Etr-end Oct Last arrival 23.00hrs Last departure noon

Located in the village of Wrelton, this well-maintained mainly seasonal touring and holiday home park is divided into small paddocks by mature hedging. The village pub and restaurant are within a few minutes walk of the park. Please note that caravans are prohibited from the A170 at Sutton Bank between Thirsk and Helmsley. A 10 acre site with 40 touring pitches, 4 hardstandings and 122 statics.

Leisure:

Facilities:

Services:

Within 3 miles:

Notes: Dogs must be kept on leads

RICHMOND

►►►► 77% Brompton Caravan Park

Brompton-on-Swale DL10 7EZ

01748 824629 01748 826383

e-mail: brompton.caravanpark@btinternet.com

dir: *Exit A1 signed Catterick, continue on B6271 to Brompton-on-Swale, site 1m on left*

* £17.50-£21 £17.50-£21 fr £17.50

Open mid Mar-Oct Last arrival 21.00hrs Last departure noon

An attractive and well-managed family park where pitches have an open outlook across the River Swale. There is a good children's playground, an excellent family recreation room, a takeaway food service, and fishing is available on the river. Newly converted holiday apartments are also available. A 14 acre site with 177 touring pitches, 2 hardstandings and 22 statics.

Leisure:

Facilities:

Services:

Within 3 miles:

Notes: No gazebos, no motor or electric cars/scooters, quiet at midnight

RIPON

►►► 80% Riverside Meadows Country Caravan Park

Ure Bank Top HG4 1JD

☎ 01765 602964 ▯ 01765 604045

e-mail: info@flowerofmay.com

dir: *On A61 at N end of bridge out of Ripon, W along river (do not cross river). Site 400yds, signed*

* £18-£25 £18-£25 ▲ £14-£25

Open Etr-Oct (rs Low-mid season bar open wknds only) Last arrival 21.00hrs Last departure noon

This pleasant, well-maintained site stands on high ground overlooking the River Ure, one mile from the town centre. The site has an excellent club with family room and quiet lounge. There is no access to the river from the site. Seasonal touring pitches. A 28 acre site with 80 touring pitches and 269 statics.

Leisure:

Facilities:

Services:

Within 3 miles:

Notes: Dogs allowed by arrangement only

ROBIN HOOD'S BAY

►►►► 75% Middlewood Farm Holiday Park

Middlewood Ln, Fylingthorpe YO22 4UF

☎ 01947 880414 ▯ 01947 880871

e-mail: info@middlewoodfarm.com

dir: *From A171 towards Robin Hood's Bay & into Fylingthorpe. Site signed from A171*

* £13-£22 £13-£22 ▲ £11-£19

Open Mar-Oct Last arrival 21.00hrs Last departure noon

A peaceful, friendly family park in a picturesque fishing village enjoying panoramic views over Robin Hood's Bay. The park has two toilet blocks with private facilities. The village pub is a 5-minute walk away, and the beach is a 10-minute walk. A 7 acre site with 100 touring pitches, 19 hardstandings and 30 statics.

Leisure:

Facilities:

Services:

Within 3 miles:

Notes: Dogs must be kept on leads at all times, dangerous breeds not accepted. No radios/noise after 22.00hrs. Pot wash sinks

ROBIN HOOD'S BAY

►►► 79% Grouse Hill Caravan Park

Flask Bungalow Farm, Fylingdales YO22 4QH

☎ 01947 880543 & 880560

01947 880543

e-mail: info@grousehill.co.uk

dir: *Off A171 (Whitby-Scarborough road), entered via loop road at Flask Inn*

Open Mar-Oct (rs Etr-May shop & reception restricted) Last arrival 21.00hrs Last departure noon

A spacious family park on a south-facing slope, with many terraced pitches overlooking the North Yorkshire Moors National Park. The owners are constantly improving the park, and it is an ideal base for walking and touring. A 14 acre site with 175 touring pitches, 30 hardstandings.

Leisure:

Facilities:

Services:

Within 3 miles:

Notes: Dogs must be kept on leads at all times. Fish & chip van on Saturdays from 20.15hrs

ROSEDALE ABBEY

►►►► 74% Rosedale Caravan & Camping Park

YO18 8SA

☎ 01751 417272

e-mail: info@flowerofmay.com

dir: *From Pickering take A170 towards Sinnington for 2.25m. At Wrelton turn right onto unclass road signed Cropton & Rosedale, 7m. Site on left in village*

* £18-£25 £18-£25 £14-£25

Open Mar-Oct Last arrival 21.00hrs Last departure noon

Set in a sheltered valley in the centre of the North Yorkshire Moors National Park, and divided into separate areas for tents, tourers and statics. A very popular park, with well-tended grounds, and close to the pretty village of Rosedale Abbey. Two toilet blocks offer private, combined facilities. A 10 acre site with 100 touring pitches and 35 statics.

Leisure:

Facilities:

Services:

Within 3 miles:

Notes: Dogs allowed by arrangement only

SCARBOROUGH

►►►►► 75% Jacobs Mount Caravan Park

Jacobs Mount, Stepney Rd YO12 5NL
☎ 01723 361178 Fax 01723 361178
e-mail: jacobsmount@yahoo.co.uk
dir: *Direct access from A170*

* £11-£19.50 £11-£19.50
£11-£19.50

Open Mar-Nov (rs Mar-May & Oct limited hours at shop/bar) Last arrival 22.00hrs Last departure noon

An elevated family-run park surrounded by woodland and open countryside, yet only two miles from the beach. Touring pitches are terraced gravel stands with individual services. A licensed bar and family room provide meals and snacks, and there is a separate well-equipped games room for teenagers. An 18 acre site with 156 touring pitches, 131 hardstandings and 60 statics.

Leisure:
Facilities:
Services:
Within 3 miles:
Notes: Pets must be kept on leads. Food preparation area

SCARBOROUGH

►►►► 77% Scarborough Camping & Caravanning Club Site

Field Ln, Burniston Rd YO13 0DA
☎ 01723 366212
dir: *On W side of A165, 1m N of Scarborough*

Open Apr-2 Nov Last arrival 21.00hrs Last departure noon

A spacious site where the majority of pitches are hardstandings of plastic webbing which allow the grass to grow through naturally. This is an excellent family-orientated park with its own shop and takeaway, within easy reach of the resort of Scarborough. A 20 acre site with 300 touring pitches, 100 hardstandings.

Leisure:
Facilities:
Services:
Within 3 miles:

SCARBOROUGH

►►► 78% Killerby Old Hall

Killerby YO11 3TW

☎ 01723 583799 01723 581608

e-mail: killerbyhall@btconnect.com

dir: *Direct access via B1261 at Killerby, near Cayton*

£17.50-£22 £17.50-£22

Open 14 Feb-4 Jan Last arrival 20.00hrs Last departure noon

A small secluded park, well sheltered by mature trees and shrubs, located at the rear of the old hall. Use of the small indoor swimming pool is shared by visitors to the hall's holiday accommodation. There is a children's play area. A 2 acre site with 20 touring pitches, 20 hardstandings.

Leisure:

Facilities:

Services:

Within 3 miles:

SELBY

►►► 79% The Ranch Caravan Park

Cliffe Common YO8 6EF

☎ 01757 638984 01757 630089

e-mail: contact@theranchcaravanpark.co.uk

dir: *Exit A63 at Cliffe signed Skipwith. Site 1m N on left*

* £14.50-£16.50 £14.50-£16.50 £14.50-£16.50

Open 5 Feb-5 Jan Last arrival 20.00hrs Last departure noon

A compact, sheltered park in open countryside offering excellent amenities. The enthusiastic and welcoming family owners have created a country club feel, with a tasteful bar serving food at weekends. A 7 acre site with 50 touring pitches, 50 hardstandings.

Leisure:

Facilities:

Services:

Within 3 miles:

Notes: Wi-fi

SLINGSBY

►►►► 76% Robin Hood Caravan & Camping Park

Green Dyke Ln YO62 4AP

☎ 01653 628391 🖷 01653 628392

e-mail: info@robinhoodcaravanpark.co.uk

dir: *On edge of Slingsby. Access off B1257 (Malton-Helmsley road)*

* £15-£25 £15-£25 £15-£25

Open Mar-Oct Last arrival 18.00hrs Last departure noon

A pleasant, well-maintained grassy park, in a good position for touring North Yorkshire. Situated on the edge of the village of Slingsby, the park has hardstandings and electricity for every pitch. A 2 acre site with 32 touring pitches, 22 hardstandings and 35 statics.

Leisure:

Facilities:

Services:

Within 3 miles:

Notes: Caravan hire, off-licence

STAINFORTH

►►►► 78% Knight Stainforth Hall Caravan & Campsite

BD24 0DP

☎ 01729 822200 🖷 01729 823387

e-mail: info@knightstainforth.co.uk

dir: *From W, on A65 take B6480 for Settle, left before swimming pool signed Little Stainforth. From E, through Settle on B6480, over bridge to swimming pool, then turn right*

* £15-£17 £15-£17 £15-£17

Open Mar-Oct Last arrival 22.00hrs Last departure noon

Located near Settle and the River Ribble in the Yorkshire Dales National Park, this well-maintained family site is sheltered by mature woodland. It is an ideal base for walking or touring in the beautiful surrounding areas. The toilet block is appointed to a very high standard. A 6 acre site with 100 touring pitches, 27 hardstandings and 60 statics.

Leisure:

Facilities:

Services:

Within 3 miles:

Notes: No groups of unaccompanied minors. Fishing. Wi-fi

SUTTON-ON-THE-FOREST

►►►► 83% Goosewood Caravan Park

YO61 1ET

☎ 01347 810829 01347 811498

e-mail: edward@goosewood.co.uk

dir: *From A1237 take B1363. After 5m turn right. Take right turn after 0.5m & site on right*

Open Feb-14 Jan Last arrival 20.00hrs Last departure noon

An immaculately maintained park with its own lake and seasonal fishing, set in attractive woodland just six miles north of York. The generous patio pitches are randomly spaced throughout the site, and there's a good play area for younger children, with a recreation barn for teenagers, plus a health spa. A 20 acre site with 75 touring pitches, 75 hardstandings and 35 statics.

Leisure:

Facilities:

Services:

Within 3 miles:

THIRSK

►►► 64% Sowerby Caravan Park

Sowerby YO7 3AG

☎ 01845 522753 01845 574520

e-mail: sowerbycaravans@btconnect.com

dir: *From A19 approx 3m S of Thirsk, turn W for Sowerby. Turn right at junct. Site 1m on left*

* £10.20-£11.50 £10.20-£11.50

Open Mar-Oct Last arrival 22.00hrs

A grassy site beside a tree-lined river bank, with basic but functional toilet facilities. Tourers enjoy a separate grassed area with an open outlook, away from the statics. A 1 acre site with 25 touring pitches, 5 hardstandings and 85 statics.

Leisure:

Facilities:

Services:

Within 3 miles:

Notes:

WYKEHAM

►►►► 83%

St Helens Caravan Park

YO13 9QD

☎ 01723 862771 🖹 01723 866613

e-mail: caravans@wykeham.co.uk

dir: *On A170 in village, 150yds on left beyond Downe Arms Hotel towards Scarborough*

* £14.90-£19.90 £14.90-£19.90 £10.90-£18

Open 15 Feb-15 Jan (rs Nov-Jan shop/laundry closed) Last arrival 22.00hrs Last departure 17.00hrs

Set on the edge of the North York Moors National Park this delightfully landscaped park is well-maintained and thoughtfully laid out with top quality facilities. The site is divided into terraces with tree-screening creating smaller areas, including an adults' zone. A cycle route leads through the surrounding Wykeham Estate, and there is a short pathway to the adjoining Downe Arms country pub. A 25 acre site with 250 touring pitches, 10 hardstandings.

Leisure: Facilities: Services:

Within 3 miles:

Notes: Caravan storage. Wi-fi

CASTEL

►►►► 80%

Fauxquets Valley Campsite

GY5 7QL

☎ 01481 236951 & 07781 413333

e-mail: info@fauxquets.co.uk

dir: *From pier. 2nd exit off rdbt. Top of hill left onto Queens Rd. Continue for 2m. Turn right onto Candie Rd. Opposite sign for German Occupation Museum*

* £12.80-£16.80

Open mid Jun-Aug

A beautiful, quiet farm site in a hidden valley close to the sea. Friendly helpful owners, who understand campers' needs, offer good quality facilities and amenities, including upgraded toilets, an outdoor swimming pool, bar/restaurant, nature trail and sports areas. A 3 acre site with 120 touring pitches.

Leisure:

Facilities:

Services:

Within 3 miles:

Notes: Birdwatching

VALE

►►► 80% La Bailloterie Camping & Leisure

Bailloterie Ln GY3 5HA

☎ 01481 243636 & 07781 103420

01481 243225

e-mail: info@campinginguernsey.com

dir: *3m N of St Peter Port, take Vale road to Crossways, turn right into Rue du Braye. Site 1st left at sign*

Open 15 May-15 Sep Last arrival 23.00hrs

A pretty rural site with one large touring field and a few small, well-screened paddocks. This delightful site has been in the same family ownership for over 30 years, and offers super facilities in converted outbuildings. A 12 acre site with 100 touring pitches.

Leisure:

Facilities:

Services:

Within 3 miles:

Notes: Dogs by arrangement only. Volleyball net, boules pitch

ST MARTIN

►►►►► 80% Beuvelande Camp Site

Beuvelande JE3 6EZ

☎ 01534 853575 01534 857788

e-mail: info@campingjersey.com

web: www.campingjersey.com

dir: *Take A6 from St Helier to St Martin & follow signs to site before St Martins Church*

Open Apr-Sep (rs Apr-May & Sep pool & restaurant shut, shop hours ltd)

A well-established site with excellent toilet facilities, accessed via narrow lanes in peaceful countryside close to St Martin. An attractive bar/restaurant is the focal point of the park, especially in the evenings, and there is a small swimming pool and playground. Motorhomes and towed caravans will be met at the ferry and escorted to the site if requested when booking. A 6 acre site with 150 touring pitches and 75 statics.

Leisure:

Facilities:

Services:

Within 3 miles:

ST MARTIN

►►►► 82% Rozel Camping Park

Summerville Farm JE3 6AX

☎ 01534 855200 📠 01534 856127

e-mail: rozelcampingpark@jerseymail.co.uk

web: www.rozelcamping.co.uk

dir: *Take A6 from St Helier through Five Oaks to St Martins Church, turn right onto A38 towards Rozel, site on right*

Open May-mid Sep Last departure noon

Customers can be sure of a warm welcome on this family-run park. Set in the north east of the island, it offers large spacious pitches, many with electric, for tents, caravans and motorhomes. Rozel Bay is just a short distance away and spectacular views of the French coast can be seen from one of the four fields on the park. The site also offers excellent facilities. Motorhomes and caravans will be met at the ferry and escorted to the park by arrangement when booking. A 4 acre site with 100 touring pitches and 20 statics.

Leisure: **Facilities:** **Services:** **Within 3 miles:**

Notes: Dogs allowed only during low season. Mini golf

ST OUEN

►►►► 79% Bleu Soleil Campsite

La Route de Vinchelez, Leoville JE3 2DB

☎ 01534 481007 📠 01534 481525

e-mail: info@bleusoleilcamping.com

web: www.bleusoleilcamping.com

dir: *From St Helier ferry port take A2 towards St Aubin then turn right onto A12 passing airport to Leoville. Site on right of La Route de Vinchelez*

* £12-£34 £12-£81

Open all year Last arrival 23.00hrs Last departure 10.00hrs

A compact tent park set in the NW corner of the island and surrounded by beautiful countryside. Greve-de-Lacq beach is close by, and the golden beaches at St Ouen's Bay and St Brelade's Bay are only a short drive away. There are 45 ready-erected tents and 6 family tipis for hire. A 1.5 acre site with 55 touring pitches, 8 hardstandings and 45 statics.

Leisure:

Facilities:

Services:

Within 3 miles:

Notes: No noise after 22.00hrs. Owners must clean up after dogs. Hot tub. Wi-fi

KIRK MICHAEL

►►► 76% Glen Wyllin Campsite

IM6 1AL

☎ 01624 878231 & 878836

01624 878836

e-mail: michaelcommissioners@manx.net

dir: *From Douglas take A1 to Ballacraine, right at lights onto A3 to Kirk Michael. Left onto A4 signed Peel. Site 100yds on right*

Open Apr-mid Sep Last departure noon

Set in a beautiful wooded glen with bridges over a pretty stream dividing the camping areas. A gently-sloping tarmac road gives direct access to a good beach. Hire tents available. A 9 acre site with 90 touring pitches and 18 statics.

Leisure:

Facilities:

Services:

Within 3 miles:

Notes: No excess noise after midnight. Dogs must be kept under control & on leads. Wi-fi

ABOYNE

►►► 69% Aboyne Loch Caravan Park

AB34 5BR

☎ 013398 86244 & 01330 811351

013398 86244

dir: *On A93, 1m E of Aboyne*

* fr £16 fr £16 fr £11

Open 31 Mar-Oct Last arrival 20.00hrs Last departure 11.00hrs

Attractively sited caravan park set amidst woodland on the shores of the lovely Aboyne Loch in scenic Deeside. The facilities are modern and immaculately maintained, and amenities include boat-launching, boating and fishing. An ideally situated park for touring Royal Deeside and the Aberdeenshire uplands. A 6 acre site with 20 touring pitches, 25 hardstandings and 120 statics.

Leisure:

Facilities:

Services:

Within 3 miles:

Notes: Coarse & pike fishing, boats for hire

HUNTLY

►►►► 85%

Huntly Castle Caravan Park

The Meadow AB54 4UJ

☎ 01466 794999

e-mail: enquiries@huntlycastle.co.uk

web: www.huntlycastle.co.uk

dir: *From Aberdeen on A96 to Huntly. 0.75m after rdbt (on outskirts of Huntly) right towards town centre, left into Riverside Drive*

Open Apr-Oct Last arrival 20.00hrs Last departure noon

A quality parkland site within striking distance of the Speyside Malt Whisky Trail, the beautiful Moray coast, and the Cairngorm Mountains. The park provides exceptional toilet facilities, and there are some fully serviced pitches. The Indoor Activity Centre provides a wide range of games; the attractive town of Huntly with its ruined castle is only 5 minutes' walk away, with a wide variety of restaurants and shops. A 15 acre site with 90 touring pitches, 46 hardstandings and 40 statics.

Leisure: **Facilities:** **Services:** **Within 3 miles:** **Notes:** Badminton, table tennis

MACDUFF

►► 65%

Wester Bonnyton Farm Site

Gamrie AB45 3EP

☎ 01261 832470 01261 831853

e-mail: westerbonnyton@fsmail.net

dir: *From A98 (1m S of Macduff) take B9031 signed Rosehearty. Site 1.25m on right*

Open Mar-Oct

A spacious farm site in a screened meadow, with level touring pitches enjoying views across Moray Firth. The site is continually improving, and offers some electric hook-ups and a laundry. An 8 acre site with 10 touring pitches, 5 hardstandings and 50 statics.

Leisure:

Facilities:

Services:

Within 3 miles:

Notes: Children's playbarn

NORTH WATER BRIDGE

►►► 74% Dovecot Caravan Park

AB30 1QL

☎ 01674 840630 Fax 01674 840630

e-mail: adele@dovecotcaravanpark.co.uk

dir: *Take A90, 5m S of Laurencekirk. At Edzell Woods sign turn left. Site 500yds on left*

* £11.50-£12.50 £11.50-£12.50 £7.50-£9.50

Open Apr-Oct Last arrival 20.00hrs Last departure noon

A level grassy site in a country area close to the A90, with mature trees screening one side and the River North Esk on the other. The immaculate toilet facilities make this a handy overnight stop in a good touring area. A 6 acre site with 25 touring pitches, 8 hardstandings and 44 statics.

Leisure:

Facilities:

Services:

Within 3 miles:

Notes: Wi-fi

TARLAND

►►► 77% Tarland Camping & Caravanning Club Site

AB34 4UP

☎ 01339 881388

dir: *A93 from Aberdeen turn right in Aboyne at Struan Hotel onto B9094. In 6m next right, then fork left before bridge, site 600yds on left*

Open 2 Apr-2 Nov Last arrival 21.00hrs Last departure noon

A pretty park on the edge of the village, laid out on two levels. The upper area has hardstandings and electric hook-ups, and views over hills and moorland, while the lower level is well screened with mature trees and is grassy. An 8 acre site with 58 touring pitches, 32 hardstandings and 40 statics.

Leisure:

Facilities:

Services:

Within 3 miles:

MONIFIETH

►►►► 78%

Riverview Caravan Park

Marine Dr DD5 4NN

☎ 01382 535471 01382 811525

e-mail: info@riverview.co.uk

web: www.riverview.co.uk

dir: *From Dundee on A930 follow signs to Monifieth, past supermarket, right signed golf course, right under rail bridge. Site signed on left*

Open Apr-Oct Last arrival 22.00hrs Last departure 12.30hrs

A well-landscaped seaside site with individual hedged pitches, and direct access to the beach. The modernised toilet block has excellent facilities which are immaculately maintained. Amenities include a multi-gym, sauna and steam rooms. 46 seasonal touring pitches available. A 5.5 acre site with 40 touring pitches, 40 hardstandings and 46 statics.

Leisure:

Facilities:

Services:

Within 3 miles:

GLENDARUEL

►►► 77%

Glendaruel Caravan Park

PA22 3AB

☎ 01369 820267 01369 820367

e-mail: mail@glendaruelcaravanpark.com

web: www.glendaruelcaravanpark.com

dir: *A83 onto A815 to Strachur, 13m to site on A886. By ferry from Gourock to Dunoon then B836, then A886 for approx 4m N. (NB this route not recommended for towing vehicles. 1:5 uphill gradient on B836)*

* £16 £16-£19 £12-£19

Open Apr-Oct Last arrival 22.00hrs Last departure noon

A pleasant site in the gardens of Glendaruel House, run by friendly owners. Level grass and hardstanding pitches are set in wooded parkland in a valley surrounded by mountains. Static caravans for hire and seasonal touring pitches available. A 3 acre site with 25 touring pitches, 15 hardstandings and 33 statics.

Leisure: **Facilities:** **Services:** **Within 3 miles:** **Notes:** Dogs must be on leads at all times. Sea trout & salmon fishing, woodland walks, 24-hour emergency phone available. Wi-fi

OBAN

►►► 78% Oban Caravan & Camping Park

Gallanachmore Farm, Gallanach Rd PA34 4QH

☎ 01631 562425 Fax 01631 566624

dir: *From Oban centre follow signs for Mull Ferry. Take turn past terminal signed Gallanach. 2m to site*

Open Etr/Apr-Oct Last arrival 23.00hrs Last departure noon

A tourist park in an attractive location close to sea and ferries. This family park is a popular base for walking, sea based activities and for those who just want to enjoy the peace and tranquillity. Self-catering holiday lodges for hire. A 15 acre site with 150 touring pitches, 35 hardstandings and 12 statics.

Leisure:

Facilities:

Services:

Within 3 miles:

Notes: Indoor kitchen for tent campers

BRIGHOUSE BAY

►►►►► 93% Brighouse Bay Holiday Park

DG6 4TS

☎ 01557 870267 Fax 01557 870319

e-mail: aa@brighouse-bay.co.uk

dir: *Off B727 (Kirkcudbright to Borgue) or take A755 (Kirkcudbright) off A75 2m W of Twynholm. Site signed*

Open all year (rs Nov-Mar leisure club closed 2 days each week) Last arrival 21.30hrs Last departure 11.30hrs

This grassy site enjoys a coastal setting next to the beach with superb sea views. Pitches have been sculpted into the meadowland, with stone walls and hedges blending in with the site's mature trees. These features, together with the large range of leisure activities, make this an excellent park. Many of the facilities are at an extra charge. A range of self-catering units is available for hire. A 30 acre site with 190 touring pitches and 120 statics.

Leisure: **Facilities:** **Services:** **Within 3 miles:**

Notes: Mini golf, 18-hole golf, riding, fishing, quad bikes

CREETOWN

►►►►► 84% Castle Cary Holiday Park

DG8 7DQ

☎ 01671 820264 🖷 01671 820670

e-mail: enquiries@castlecarypark.f9.co.uk

web: www.castlecary-caravans.com

dir: *Signed with direct access off A75, 0.5m S of village*

Open all year (rs Oct-Mar reception/shop, no heated outdoor pool) Last arrival anytime Last departure noon

Set in the grounds of Cassencarie House this site is sheltered by woodlands, and faces south towards Wigtown Bay. The park has beautiful landscaping and excellent facilities. The bar/restaurant is housed in an old castle, and enjoys views over the River Cree estuary. A 12 acre site with 50 touring pitches, 50 hardstandings and 26 statics.

Leisure: **Facilities:** **Services:** **Within 3 miles:**

Notes: Dogs must be kept on leads at all times. Bike hire, crazy golf, coarse fishing, full size football pitch

CROCKETFORD

►►►► 84% The Park of Brandedleys

DG2 8RG

☎ 01387 266700 🖷 01556 690681

e-mail: brandedleys@holgates.com

web: www.holgates.com

dir: *In village on A75, from Dumfries towards Stranraer site on left 200yds on right*

Open all year (rs Nov-Mar bar/restaurant open Fri-Sun afternoon) Last arrival 22.00hrs Last departure noon

A well-maintained site in an elevated position off the A75, with fine views of Auchenreoch Loch and beyond. This comfortable park offers a wide range of amenities, including a fine games room and a tastefully-designed bar with adjoining bistro. There are holiday homes for sale and hire on this park, which is well placed for enjoying walking, fishing, sailing and golf. A 24 acre site with 80 touring pitches, 40 hardstandings and 63 statics.

Leisure: **Facilities:** **Services:** **Within 3 miles:**

Notes: Guidelines issued on arrival. Badminton court

DALBEATTIE

►►►► 79%

Glenearly Caravan Park

DG5 4NE

☎ 01556 611393 01556 612058

e-mail: glenearlycaravan@btconnect.com

dir: *From Dumfries take A711 towards Dalbeattie. Site entrance after Edingham Farm on right (200yds before boundary sign)*

£13.50-£15.50

Open all year Last arrival 19.00hrs Last departure noon

An excellent small park set in open countryside with panoramic views of Long Fell, Maidenpap and Dalbeattie Forest. The park is located in 84 acres of farmland which visitors are invited to enjoy. Luxury extras are provided in the laundry and toilets, including washing powder and conditioner, sachets of shampoo and shower gel, pegs and washing lines, washing-up liquid, brushes and cloths in the dish-washing area. Static holiday caravans for hire. A 10 acre site with 39 touring pitches, 33 hardstandings and 74 statics.

Leisure: **Facilities:** **Services:** **Within 3 miles:** **Notes:** No commercial vehicles, dogs must be kept on leads

ECCLEFECHAN

►►►►► 77%

Hoddom Castle Caravan Park

Hoddom DG11 1AS

☎ 01576 300251 01576 300757

e-mail: hoddomcastle@aol.com

dir: *M74 junct 19, follow signs to site. From A75 W of Annan take B723 for 5m, follow signs to site*

* £9-£19 £9-£19 £8-£16

Open Etr or Apr-Oct (rs Early season cafeteria closed) Last arrival 21.00hrs Last departure 14.00hrs

The peaceful, well-equipped park can be found on the banks of the River Annan, and offers a good mix of grassy and hardstanding pitches, beautifully landscaped and blending into the surroundings. There are signed nature trails, maintained by the park's ranger, a 9-hole golf course, trout and salmon fishing, and plenty of activity ideas for children. A 28 acre site with 200 touring pitches, 150 hardstandings and 54 statics.

Leisure: **Facilities:** **Services:** **Within 3 miles:**

Notes: No electric scooters. Visitor centre

GATEHOUSE OF FLEET

82% Auchenlarie Holiday Park

DG7 2EX

☎ 01557 840251 🖷 01557 840333

e-mail: enquiries@auchenlarie.co.uk

web: www.auchenlarie.co.uk

dir: *Direct access off A75, 5m W of Gatehouse of Fleet*

* £15-£30 £15-£30 £15-£30

Open Mar-Oct Last arrival 20.00hrs Last departure noon

A well-organised family park set on cliffs overlooking Wigtown Bay, with its own sandy beach. The tenting area, in sloping grass surrounded by mature trees, has its own sanitary facilities, while the marked caravan pitches are in paddocks with open views, and enjoy high quality toilets. The leisure centre includes swimming pool, gym, solarium and sports hall. The park also has an extensive selection of holiday homes for hire. A 32 acre site with 49 touring pitches, 49 hardstandings and 350 statics.

Leisure: **Facilities:** **Services:** **Within 3 miles:**

Notes: Baby changing facilities

GRETNA

►►►► 74% King Robert the Bruce's Cave C&C Park

Cove Estate, Kirkpatrick Fleming DG11 3AT

☎ 01461 800285 & 07779 138694

🖷 01461 800269

e-mail: enquiries@brucescave.co.uk

web: www.brucescave.co.uk

dir: *A74(M) junct 21 for Kirkpatrick Fleming, N through village, pass Station Inn, left at Bruce's Court. Over rail crossing to site*

* £12.50 £12.50 £10-£20

Open Apr-Nov (rs Nov-Mar shop closed, water restriction) Last arrival 22.00hrs Last departure 16.00hrs

The wooded grounds of an old castle and mansion are the setting for this park. The mature woodland is a haven for wildlife, and there is a riverside walk to Robert the Bruce's Cave. A toilet block with en suite facilities is great for families. 60 seasonal touring pitches available. An 80 acre site with 75 touring pitches, 60 hardstandings and 35 statics.

Leisure: **Facilities:** **Services:** **Within 3 miles:**

Notes: Dogs must be kept on leads. BMX bike hire, coarse fishing, first aid available

KIPPFORD

►►► 79% Kippford Holiday Park

DG5 4LF

☎ 01556 620636 01556 620607

e-mail: info@kippfordholidaypark.co.uk

dir: *From Dumfries take A711 to Dalbeattie, left onto A710 (Solway coast road) for 3.5m. Park 200yds beyond Kippford turn on right*

£19-£25 £19-£25 £17-£23

Open all year Last arrival 21.30hrs Last departure noon

An attractively landscaped park set in hilly countryside close to the Urr Water estuary and a sand/shingle beach, and with spectacular views. The level touring pitches are on grassed hardstandings with private garden areas, and many are fully serviced, and there are some very attractive lodges for hire. The Doon Hill and woodland walks separate the park from the lovely village of Kippford. An 18 acre site with 45 touring pitches, 22 hardstandings and 119 statics.

Leisure:

Facilities:

Services:

Within 3 miles:

Notes: No camp fires. Golf, fly fishing, nature walk, cycle hire. Wi-fi

KIRKCUDBRIGHT

►►►► 82% Seaward Caravan Park

Dhoon Bay DG6 4TJ

☎ 01557 870267 & 870319

01557 870319

e-mail: aa@seaward-park.co.uk

dir: *2m SW off B727 (Borgue road)*

* £16.40-£21.70 £16.40-£21.70 £12.30-£17.60

Open Mar-Oct (rs Mar-mid May & mid Sep-Oct swimming pool closed) Last arrival 21.30hrs Last departure 11.30hrs

Elevated park with outstanding views over Kirkcudbright Bay, which is part of the Dee Estuary. Access to a sandy cove with rock pools is nearby. Facilities are neatly kept, and the park offers a very peaceful atmosphere. Leisure facilities at the other Gillespie parks are available to visitors here. 6 touring pitches available. An 8 acre site with 26 touring pitches, 20 hardstandings and 54 statics.

Leisure: **Facilities:** **Services:**

Within 3 miles:

Notes: No motorised scooters or bikes (except disabled vehicles). Pets must be kept on leads. Pitch & putt, volley ball, badminton, table tennis

PALNACKIE

►►► 79% Barlochan Caravan Park

DG7 1PF

☎ 01556 600256 & 01557 870267
01557 870319

e-mail: aa@barlochan.co.uk

dir: *On A711, N of Palnackie, signed*

Open Apr-Oct Last arrival 21.30hrs Last departure 11.30hrs

A small terraced park with quiet landscaped pitches in a level area backed by rhododendron bushes. There are spectacular views over the River Urr estuary, and the park has its own coarse fishing loch nearby. The amenity block has been upgraded to include combined wash facilities. A 9 acre site with 20 touring pitches, 3 hardstandings and 65 statics.

Leisure:

Facilities:

Services:

Within 3 miles:

Notes: Pitch & putt

PARTON

►►► 69% Loch Ken Holiday Park

DG7 3NE

☎ 01644 470282

e-mail: penny@lochkenholidaypark.co.uk

web: www.lochkenholidaypark.co.uk

dir: *On A713, N of Parton*

* £16-£19 £16-£19 £12-£17

Open Mar-mid Nov (rs Mar/Apr (ex Etr) & late Sep-Nov restricted shop hours) Last departure noon

A busy and popular park with a natural emphasis on water activities, set on the eastern shores of Loch Ken, with superb views. Family owned and run, it is in a peaceful and beautiful spot opposite the RSPB reserve, with direct access to the loch for fishing and boat launching. The park offers a variety of water sports, as well as farm visits and nature trails. Static caravans are for hire. A 7 acre site with 52 touring pitches, 4 hardstandings and 35 statics.

Leisure:

Facilities:

Services:

Within 3 miles:

Notes: Bike, boat & canoe hire

SANDHEAD

►►►► 74% Sands of Luce Holiday Park

Sands of Luce DG9 9JN

☎ 01776 830456 📄 01776 830477

e-mail: info@sandsofluceholidaypark.co.uk

web: www.sandsofluceholidaypark.co.uk

dir: *From S & E: left from A75 onto B7084 signed Drummore. Site signed at junct with A716. From N: A77 through Stranraer towards Portpatrick, 2m, follow A716 signed Drummore, site signed in 5m*

* £15-£20 £15-£20 £15-£20

Open Mar-Jan Last arrival 20.00hrs Last departure noon

A large park with a balance of static and touring caravans, with direct access to a sandy beach and with views across Luce Bay. The park has a boat storage area, an excellent static hire fleet and a well-managed club. 75 seasonal touring pitches. A 30 acre site with 100 touring pitches and 190 statics.

Leisure: **Facilities:** **Services:** **Within 3 miles:** **Notes:** Dogs must be kept on leads at all time & dog fouling must be cleared up. No quad bsikes. Boat launching. Play park. Wi-fi

SOUTHERNESS

79% Southerness Holiday Village

Off Sandy Ln DG2 8AZ

☎ 0844 335 3756 📄 01387 880429

e-mail: touringandcamping@parkdeanholidays.com

web: www.parkdeantouring.com

dir: *From S: A75 Gretna to Dumfries. From N: A74, exit at A701 to Dumfries. Take A710 (coast road), approx 16m, site easily visible*

* £12-£31 £12-£31 £12-£31

Open Mar-Oct Last arrival 21.00hrs Last departure 10.00hrs

There are stunning views across the Solway Firth from this holiday park at the foot of the Galloway Hills. A sandy beach on the Solway Firth is accessible directly from the park. The emphasis is on family entertainment, and facilities include all-weather pitches and an indoor pool, show bar, coast bar and kitchen. A 50 acre site with 100 touring pitches, 60 hardstandings and 611 statics.

Leisure: **Facilities:** **Services:** **Within 3 miles:** **Notes:** Amusements centre, live entertainment, children's clubs. Wi-fi

STRANRAER

►►►► 77% Aird Donald Caravan Park

London Rd DG9 8RN

☎ 01776 702025

e-mail: enquiries@aird-donald.co.uk

web: www.aird-donald.co.uk

dir: *From A75 left on entering Stranraer (signed). Opposite school, site 300yds*

Open all year Last departure 16.00hrs

A spacious touring site, mainly grass but with tarmac hardstanding areas, with pitches large enough to accommodate a car and caravan overnight without unhitching. On the fringe of town screened by mature shrubs and trees. Ideal stopover en route to Northern Irish ferry ports. A 12 acre site with 100 touring pitches, 30 hardstandings.

Leisure:

Facilities:

Services:

Within 3 miles:

Notes: Tents Apr-Sep

WIGTOWN

►►► 85% Drumroamin Farm Camping & Touring Site

1 South Balfern DG8 9DB

☎ 01988 840613 & 07752 471456

e-mail: enquiry@drumroamin.co.uk

dir: *A75 towards Newton Stewart, onto A714 for Wigtown. Left on B7005 through Bladnock, A746 through Kirkinner. Take B7004 signed Garlieston, 2nd left opposite Kilsture Forest, site 0.75m at end of lane*

* £14 £14 £12

Open all year Last arrival 21.00hrs Last departure noon

An open, spacious park in a quiet spot a mile from the main road, and close to Wigtown Bay. A superb toilet block offers spacious showers, and there's a lounge/games room and plenty of room for children to play. A 5 acre site with 48 touring pitches and 3 statics.

Leisure:

Facilities:

Services:

Within 3 miles:

Notes: No fires. Ball games area

DUNBAR

►►►►► 87% Thurston Manor Holiday Home Park

Innerwick EH42 1SA

☎ 01368 840643 01368 840261

e-mail: mail@thurstonmanor.co.uk

dir: *4m S of Dunbar, signed off A1*

* £17-£27 £17-£27 £7-£23

Open Mar-8 Jan (rs 1-22 Dec site open wknds only) Last arrival 23.00hrs Last departure noon

A pleasant park set in 250 acres of unspoilt countryside. The touring and static areas of this large park are in separate areas. The main touring area occupies an open, level position, and the toilet facilities are modern and very well maintained. The park boasts a fishing loch, a heated indoor swimming pool, steam room, sauna, jacuzzi, mini-gym and fitness room and seasonal entertainment. A 250 acre site with 100 touring pitches, 45 hardstandings and 500 statics.

Leisure:

Facilities:

Services:

Within 3 miles:

Notes: Wi-fi

LONGNIDDRY

66% Seton Sands Holiday Village

EH32 0QF

☎ 01875 813333 01875 813531

e-mail: lee.mckay@bourne-leisure.co.uk

dir: *A1 to A198 exit, then B6371 to Cockenzie. Right onto B1348. Site 1m on right*

* £8-£68 £8-£68 £8-£50

Open mid Mar-Oct (rs mid Mar-May & Sep-Oct some facilities may be reduced) Last arrival 22.00hrs Last departure 10.00hrs

A well-equipped holiday centre with plenty of organised entertainment, clubs and bars, restaurants, and sports and leisure facilities. A multi-sports court, heated swimming pool, and various play areas ensure that there is plenty to do, and there is lots to see and do in and around Edinburgh which is nearby. The good touring facilities are separate from the large static areas. A 1.75 acre site with 38 touring pitches and 635 statics.

Leisure: **Facilities:**

Services:

Within 3 miles:

Notes: Dogs not allowed at peak periods, max 2 dogs per pitch, certain dog breeds banned. Wi-fi

MUSSELBURGH

►►►► 80% Drum Mohr Caravan Park

Levenhall EH21 8JS

☎ 0131 665 6867 0131 653 6859

e-mail: admin@drummohr.org

web: www.drummohr.org

dir: *Exit A1 at A199 junct through Wallyford, at rdbt onto B1361 signed Prestonpans. 1st left, site 400yds*

* £17-£23 £17-£23 £17-£23

Open Mar-Oct Last arrival 20.00hrs Last departure noon

This attractive park is sheltered by mature trees on all sides, and carefully landscaped within. The park is divided into separate areas by mature hedging and planting of trees and ornamental shrubs. Pitches are generous in size, and there are a number of fully serviced pitches plus first-class amenities. A 9 acre site with 120 touring pitches, 50 hardstandings and 12 statics.

Leisure:

Facilities:

Services:

Within 3 miles:

Notes: Max of 2 dogs per pitch. Wi-fi

ST ANDREWS

►►►►► 91% Craigtoun Meadows Holiday Park

Mount Melville KY16 8PQ

☎ 01334 475959 01334 476424

e-mail: craigtoun@aol.com

web: www.craigtounmeadows.co.uk

dir: *M90 junct 8, A91 to St Andrews. After Guardbridge right for Strathkinness. At 2nd x-rds left for Craigtoun*

* £20-£26.50 £20-£26.50 £18

Open 15 Mar-Oct (rs Mar-Etr & Sep-Oct shops & restaurant open shorter hours) Last arrival 21.00hrs Last departure 11.00hrs

Attractive site in mature woodlands, with fully serviced pitches in hedged paddocks, situated near the sea and sandy beaches. The toilet block has spacious showers, baths, disabled facilities and baby changing areas. There's a licensed restaurant, coffee shop and takeaway. Indoor and outdoor games areas. 32 acre site with 57 touring pitches, 57 hardstandings and 166 statics.

Leisure: **Facilities:** **Services:** **Within 3 miles:**

Notes: No groups of unaccompanied minors, no pets. Putting green, football pitch

CANNICH

►►► 74%

Cannich Caravan and Camping Park

IV4 7LN

☎ 01456 415364 📠 01456 415364

e-mail: enquiries@highlandcamping.co.uk

web: www.highlandcamping.co.uk

dir: *On A831, 200yds SE of Cannich Bridge*

* £11-£14 £11-£14 £11-£14

Open Mar-Oct (rs Dec-Feb winter opening by arrangement) Last arrival 23.00hrs Last departure noon

Quietly situated in Strath Glass, close to the River Glass and Cannich village. This family-run park has attractive mountain views, and is set in ideal walking and naturalist country. There is now a café and a shop selling local crafts, on site. A 6 acre site with 43 touring pitches, 15 hardstandings and 10 statics.

Leisure:

Facilities:

Services:

Within 3 miles:

Notes: Dogs must be kept on leads. Mountain bike hire. Wi-fi

CORPACH

►►►►► 83%

Linnhe Lochside Holidays

PH33 7NL

☎ 01397 772376 📠 01397 772007

e-mail: relax@linnhe-lochside-holidays.co.uk

dir: *On A830, 1m W of Corpach, 5m from Fort William*

Open Etr-Oct Last arrival 21.00hrs Last departure 11.00hrs

An excellently maintained site in a beautiful setting on the shores of Loch Eil, with Ben Nevis to the east and the mountains and Sunart to the west. The owners have worked in harmony with nature to produce an idyllic environment, where they offer the highest standards of design and maintenance. A 5.5 acre site with 85 touring pitches, 63 hardstandings and 20 statics.

Leisure:

Facilities:

Services:

Within 3 miles:

Notes: No cars by tents. Launching slipway, free fishing

DORNOCH

76% Grannie's Heilan Hame Holiday Park

Embo IV25 3QD

☎ 0844 335 3756 🖹 01862 810368

e-mail: touringandcamping@parkdeanholidays.com

web: www.parkdeantouring.com

dir: *A949 to Dornoch, left in square. Follow Embo signs*

* £11-£29 £11-£29 £11-£29

Open Mar-Oct Last arrival 21.00hrs Last departure 10.00hrs

A holiday park on the Highland coast, with a wide range of leisure facilities, including indoor swimming pool with sauna and solarium, spa bath, separate play areas, crazy golf, tennis courts and very much more. The sanitary facilities are clean and well maintained, and there is a family pub and entertainment. A 60 acre site with 160 touring pitches and 250 statics.

Leisure:

Facilities:

Services:

Within 3 miles:

Notes: Children's clubs, mini ten-pin bowling. Wi-fi

FORT WILLIAM

►►►► 85% Glen Nevis Caravan & Camping Park

Glen Nevis PH33 6SX

☎ 01397 702191 🖹 01397 703904

e-mail: holidays@glen-nevis.co.uk

web: www.glen-nevis.co.uk

dir: *In northern outskirts of Fort William follow A82 to mini-rdbt. Exit for Glen Nevis. Site 2.5m on right*

* £11.20-£16 £11.20-£16 £10.70-£16

Open 13 Mar-9 Nov (rs Mar & mid Oct-Nov limited shop & restaurant facilities) Last arrival 22.00hrs Last departure noon

A tasteful site with well-screened enclosures, at the foot of Ben Nevis in the midst of some of the Highlands' most spectacular scenery; an ideal area for walking and touring. The park boasts a restaurant which offers a high standard of cooking and provides good value for money. A 30 acre site with 380 touring pitches, 150 hardstandings and 30 statics.

Leisure:

Facilities:

Services:

Within 3 miles:

Notes: Quiet 23.00hrs-08.00hrs

GLENCOE

►►►► 78% Invercoe Caravan & Camping Park

PH49 4HP

☎ 01855 811210 01855 811210

e-mail: holidays@invercoe.co.uk

web: www.invercoe.co.uk

dir: *Exit A82 at Glencoe Hotel onto B863 for 0.25m*

Open all year Last departure noon

Level grass site set on the shore of Loch Leven, with excellent mountain views. The area is ideal for both walking and climbing, and also offers a choice of several freshwater and saltwater lochs. Convenient for the good shopping at Fort William. A 5 acre site with 60 touring pitches and 4 statics.

Leisure:

Facilities:

Services:

Within 3 miles:

Notes: No large group bookings

NAIRN

73% Nairn Lochloy Holiday Park

East Beach IV12 5DE

☎ 0844 335 3756 01667 454721

e-mail: touringandcamping@parkdeanholidays.com

web: www.parkdeantouring.com

dir: *In Nairn, just off East Beach. On entering Nairn follow road until Bridgemill Direct shop, turn left before shop & follow signs to park*

* £10-£32 £10-£32 £10-£32

Open Mar-Oct Last arrival 21.00hrs Last departure 10.00hrs

A small touring site situated within a popular holiday park with a wide range of leisure facilities including heated pool, sauna, children's play-area and clubs, crazy golf, amusements, bars, restaurant and mini supermarket. A toilet block exclusively serves the touring area where all pitches have electricity. Handily placed in the centre of Nairn, only minutes from the beach. A 15 acre site with 13 touring pitches and 280 statics.

Leisure: **Facilities:** **Services:** **Within 3 miles:** **Notes:** Family entertainment, spa bath, sauna. Wi-fi

NAIRN

►►► 75% Nairn Camping & Caravanning Club Site

Delnies Wood IV12 5NX

☎ 01667 455281

dir: *Off A96 (Inverness to Aberdeen road). 2m W of Nairn*

Open 2 Apr-2 Nov Last arrival 21.00hrs Last departure noon

An attractive site set amongst pine trees, with facilities maintained to a good standard. The park is close to Nairn with its beaches, shopping, golf and leisure activities. A 14 acre site with 75 touring pitches.

Leisure:

Facilities:

Services:

Within 3 miles:

Notes: Site gates closed 23.00hrs-07.00hrs. Fishing

ULLAPOOL

►►► 69% Broomfield Holiday Park

West Shore St IV26 2UT

☎ 01854 612020 & 612664

01854 613151

e-mail: sross@broomfieldhp.com

web: www.broomfieldhp.com

dir: *Take 2nd right past harbour*

* £15-£16 £14-£15 £11-£16

Open Etr/Apr-Sep Last departure noon

Set right on the water's edge of Loch Broom and the open sea, with lovely views of the Summer Isles. The park is close to the harbour and town centre with their restaurants, bars and shops. A 12 acre site with 140 touring pitches.

Leisure:

Facilities:

Services:

Within 3 miles:

Notes: Pets must be kept on leads, no noise at night

ALVES

►►► 68% North Alves Caravan Park

IV30 8XD

☎ 01343 850223

dir: *1m W of A96, halfway between Elgin & Forres. Site signed on right*

Open Apr-Oct Last arrival 23.00hrs Last departure noon

A quiet rural site in attractive rolling countryside within three miles of a good beach. The site is on a former farm, and the stone buildings are quite unspoilt. A 10 acre site with 45 touring pitches and 45 statics.

Leisure:

Facilities:

Services:

Within 3 miles:

FOCHABERS

►►► 74% Burnside Caravan Park

IV32 7ET

☎ 01343 820511 01343 820511

dir: *0.5m E of town off A96*

Open Apr-Oct Last departure noon

Attractive site in a tree-lined, sheltered valley with a footpath to the village. Owned by the garden centre on the opposite side of the A96, it has five fully-serviced pitches. A 5 acre site with 51 touring pitches, 30 hardstandings and 101 statics.

Leisure:

Facilities:

Services:

Within 3 miles:

Notes: Jacuzzi & sauna

LOSSIEMOUTH

►►►► 73%
Silver Sands Leisure Park

Covesea, West Beach IV31 6SP

☎ 01343 813262 01343 815205

e-mail: holidays@silversands.freeserve.co.uk

dir: *From Lossiemouth follow B9040, 2m W to site*

Open Apr-Oct (rs Apr, May & Oct shops & entertainment restricted) Last arrival 22.00hrs Last departure noon

A large holiday park with entertainment during the peak season, set on the links beside the shore of the Moray Firth. Touring campers and caravans are catered for in three areas: one offers de-luxe, fully-serviced facilities, while the others are either unserviced or include electric hook-ups and water. There's a well-stocked shop, a clubroom and bar, and takeaway food outlet. A 7 acre site with 140 touring pitches and 200 statics.

Leisure:

Facilities:

Services:

Within 3 miles:

Notes: Over 14yrs only in bar. Children's entertainment

SALTCOATS

72% Sandylands

James Miller Crescent, Auchenharvie Park KA21 5JN

☎ 0871 664 9767

e-mail: sandylands@park-resorts.com

dir: *From Glasgow take M77 & A77 to Kilmarnock, A71 towards Irvine. Follow signs for Ardrossan. Take A78 follow Stevenston signs. Through Stevenston, past Auchenharvie Leisure Centre, 1st left follow signs to site on left*

Open Mar-Oct

Sandylands is an all action holiday centre with plenty of on-site leisure and recreational activities for the whole family. Off park, there is a links golf course adjacent, and trips to the Isle of Arran from the nearby Ardrossan. The beaches of the east coast are close by, and the mountains are just a short drive away. 20 touring pitches and 438 statics.

Leisure:

Facilities:

Services:

Within 3 miles:

BLAIR ATHOLL

►►►►► 80%

Blair Castle Caravan Park

PH18 5SR

☎ 01796 481263 01796 481587

e-mail: mail@blaircastlecaravanpark.co.uk

dir: *From A9 junct with B8079 at Aldclune, then NE to Blair Atholl. Site on right after crossing bridge in village*

* £15-£30 £15-£22 £15-£30

Open Mar-Nov Last arrival 21.30hrs Last departure noon

Attractive site set in the Atholl estate, surrounded by mature woodland and the River Tilt. Although a large park, the various groups of pitches are located throughout the extensive parkland, and each has its own sanitary block with all-cubicled facilities of a very high standard. There is a choice of grass pitches, hardstandings, or fully-serviced pitches. This park is particularly suitable for the larger type of motorhome. A 32 acre site with 280 touring pitches and 101 statics.

Leisure: **Facilities:** **Services:** **Within 3 miles:** **Notes:** Family park, no noise after 23.00hrs. Internet gallery with broadband access. Wi-fi

PITLOCHRY

►►►► 74%

Faskally Caravan Park

PH16 5LA

☎ 01796 472007 01796 473896

e-mail: info@faskally.co.uk

dir: *1.5m N of Pitlochry on B8019*

Open 15 Mar-Oct Last arrival 23.00hrs

A large park attractively divided into sections by mature trees, set in gently sloping meadowland beside the tree-lined River Garry. The excellent amenities include a leisure complex with heated indoor swimming pool, spa, sauna and steam room, bar, restaurant and indoor amusements. The park is close to, but unaffected by, the A9. A 27 acre site with 300 touring pitches and 130 statics.

Leisure:

Facilities:

Services:

Within 3 miles:

Notes: Dogs must be kept on leads

SCONE

►►► 69% Scone Camping & Caravanning Club Site

Scone Palace PH2 6BB

☎ 01738 552323

dir: *Follow signs for Scone Palace, through Perth, 2m. Turn left, follow site signs. 1m left onto Racecourse Rd. Site entrance from car park*

Open 2 Apr-2 Nov Last arrival 21.00hrs Last departure noon

A delightful woodland site, sheltered and well screened from the adjacent Scone racecourse. The two amenity blocks are built of timber and blend in well with the surroundings of mature trees. Super pitches add to the park's appeal. A 16 acre site with 150 touring pitches, 40 hardstandings.

Leisure:

Facilities:

Services:

Within 3 miles:

Notes: Site gates closed 23.00hrs-07.00hrs

TUMMEL BRIDGE

70% Tummel Valley Holiday Park

PH16 5SA

☎ 0844 335 3756 01882 634302

e-mail: touringandcamping@parkdeanholidays.com

web: www.parkdeantouring.com

dir: *From Perth take A9 N to bypass Pitlochry. 3m after Pitlochry take B8019 signed Tummel Bridge. Site 11m on left*

* £12-£30 £12-£30

Open Mar-Oct Last arrival 21.00hrs Last departure 10.00hrs

A well-developed site amongst mature forest in an attractive valley, beside the famous bridge on the banks of the River Tummel. Play areas and the bar are sited alongside the river, and there is an indoor pool, children's clubs and live family entertainment. This is an ideal base in which to relax. A 55 acre site with 34 touring pitches, 34 hardstandings and 159 statics.

Leisure: **Facilities:** **Services:** **Within 3 miles:** **Notes:** No tents or trailer tents. Sports courts, sauna, solarium, toddlers' pool, amusements, rod hire. Wi-fi

EYEMOUTH

72% Eyemouth

Fort Rd TD14 5BE

☎ 0871 664 9740

e-mail: eyemouth@park-resorts.com

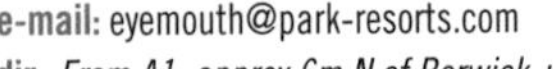

dir: *From A1, approx 6m N of Berwick-upon-Tweed take A1107 to Eyemouth. On entering town, site signed. Right after petrol station, left at bottom of hill into Fort Rd*

Open Mar-Oct (rs BH & peak wknds entertainment available)

A cliff top holiday park on the outskirts of the small fishing village of Eyemouth, within easy reach of Edinburgh and Newcastle. The site is handily placed for exploring the beautiful Scottish Borders, and the magnificent coastline and countryside of north Northumberland. 17 touring pitches and 242 statics.

Leisure:

Facilities:

Services:

Within 3 miles:

KELSO

►►►► 78% Springwood Caravan Park

TD5 8LS

☎ 01573 224596 01573 224033

e-mail: admin@springwood.biz

dir: *1m E of Kelso on A699, signed Newton St Boswells*

Open 21 Mar-13 Oct Last arrival 23.00hrs

Set in a secluded position on the banks of the tree-lined River Teviot, this well-maintained site enjoys a pleasant and spacious spot in which to relax. It offers a high standard of modern toilet facilities which are mainly contained in cubicled units. Floors Castle and the historic town of Kelso are close by. A 2 acre site with 20 touring pitches, 20 hardstandings and 212 statics.

Leisure:

Facilities:

Services:

Within 3 miles:

Notes: Dogs must be kept on leads

PEEBLES

►►►► 78% Crossburn Caravan Park

Edinburgh Rd EH45 8ED

☎ 01721 720501 🖹 01721 720501

e-mail: enquiries@crossburncaravans.co.uk

web: www.crossburncaravans.co.uk

dir: *0.5m N of Peebles on A703*

fr £18 fr £18 fr £16

Open Apr-Oct Last arrival 21.00hrs Last departure 14.00hrs

A peaceful site in a relatively quiet location, despite the proximity of the main road which partly borders the site, as does the Eddleston Water. There are lovely views, and the park is well stocked with trees, flowers and shrubs. Facilities are maintained to a high standard, and fully-serviced pitches are available. A large caravan dealership is on the same site. A 6 acre site with 45 touring pitches, 15 hardstandings and 85 statics.

Leisure:

Facilities:

Services:

Within 3 miles:

Notes: Dogs must be kept on leads

AYR

75% Craig Tara Holiday Park

KA7 4LB

☎ 01292 265141 🖹 01292 445206

e-mail: donna.moulton@bourne-leisure.co.uk

dir: *Take A77 towards Stranraer, then 2nd right after Bankfield rdbt. Follow signs to A719 & to park*

* £12-£71 £12-£71

Open mid Mar-Oct (rs mid Mar-May & Sep-Oct some facilities may be limited) Last arrival 20.00hrs Last departure 10.00hrs

A large, well-maintained holiday centre with on-site entertainment and sporting facilities for all ages. The touring area is set apart from the main complex at the entrance to the park, and campers can use all the facilities, including water world, soft play areas, sports zone, show bars and supermarket. There is a bus service to Ayr. Seasonal touring pitches available. A 213 acre site with 38 touring pitches, 38 hardstandings and 1100 statics.

Leisure: **Facilities:** **Services:** **Within 3 miles:** **Notes:** Max 2 dogs per pitch, certain dog breeds banned. Access to beach from park. Wi-fi

COYLTON

78% Sundrum Castle Holiday Park

KA6 5JH

☎ 0844 335 3756 01292 570065

e-mail: touringandcamping@parkdeanholidays.com

web: www.parkdeantouring.com

dir: *Just off A70, 4m E of Ayr near Coylton*

* £13-£32 £13-£32 £13-£32

Open Mar-Oct Last arrival 21.00hrs Last departure 10.00hrs

A large family holiday park in rolling countryside, with plenty of on-site entertainment, and just a 10-minute drive from the centre of Ayr. Leisure facilities include an indoor swimming pool complex with flume, crazy golf, clubs for young children and teenagers. The touring pitch areas and amenity block have been upgraded to a high standard. A 30 acre site with 45 touring pitches, 30 hardstandings and 67 statics.

Leisure: **Facilities:** **Services:** **Within 3 miles:**

Notes: No cars by tents. Amusements, family entertainment, adventure play area, nature trail. Wi-fi

ABERFOYLE

►►►► 78% Trossachs Holiday Park

FK8 3SA

☎ 01877 382614 01877 382732

e-mail: info@trossachsholidays.co.uk

web: www.trossachsholidays.co.uk

dir: *Access on E side of A81, 1m S of junct A821 & 3m S of Aberfoyle*

* £14-£20 £14-£20 £14-£20

Open Mar-Oct Last arrival 21.00hrs Last departure noon

An imaginatively designed terraced site offering a high degree of quality all round, with fine views across Flanders Moss. All touring pitches are fully serviced with water, waste, electricity and TV aerial, and customer care is a main priority. Set in grounds within the Queen Elizabeth Forest Park, with plenty of opportunities for cycling off-road on mountain bikes, which can be hired or purchased on site. There are self-catering units including lodges for rental. A 40 acre site with 66 touring pitches, 46 hardstandings and 84 statics.

Leisure: **Facilities:** **Services:** **Within 3 miles:**

BALMAHA

►►►► 79% Milarrochy Bay Camping & Caravanning Club Site

Milarrochy Bay G63 0AL

☎ 01360 870236

dir: *Take A811 (Balloch to Stirling road) to Drymen. In Drymen take B837 for Balmaha. In 5m road turns sharp right up steep hill. Site in 1.5m*

Open 2 Apr-2 Nov Last arrival 21.00hrs Last departure noon

On the quieter side of Loch Lomond next to the 75,000-acre Queen Elizabeth Forest, this attractive site offers very good facilities. Disabled toilets and family rooms are appointed to a high standard. Towing vehicles should engage low gear immediately at steep hill warning sign in Balmaha. A 12 acre site with 150 touring pitches, 23 hardstandings.

Leisure:

Facilities:

Services:

Within 3 miles:

Notes: Site gates closed 23.00hrs-07.00hrs. Fishing, boat launching

BALLOCH

►►►► 80% Lomond Woods Holiday Park

Old Luss Rd G83 8QP

☎ 01389 755000 01389 755563

e-mail: lomondwoods@holiday-parks.co.uk

web: www.holiday-parks.co.uk

dir: *From A82, 17m N of Glasgow, take A811 (Stirling to Balloch road). Left at 1st rdbt, follow holiday park signs, 150yds on left*

* £18-£22 £18-£22

Open all year Last arrival 20.00hrs Last departure noon

Mature park with well-laid out pitches and self-catering lodges screened by trees and shrubs, surrounded by woodland and hills. Within walking distance of 'Loch Lomond Shores', a leisure and retail complex which is the main gateway to Scotland's first National Park. Amenities include the Loch Lomond Aquarium, an Interactive Exhibition, and loch cruises. A 13 acre site with 110 touring pitches, 110 hardstandings and 35 statics.

Leisure:

Facilities:

Services:

Within 3 miles:

Notes: No tents, no jet skis. Wi-fi

LINLITHGOW

►►►► 79% Beecraigs C&C Site

Beecraigs Country Park,
The Park Centre EH49 6PL

☎ 01506 844516 01506 846256

e-mail: mail@beecraigs.com

web: www.beecraigs.com

dir: *From Linlithgow on A803 or from Bathgate on B792, follow signs to country park. Reception either at restaurant or park centre*

* £13.65-£15.85 £13.65-£15.85 £12-£19.70

Open all year (rs 25-26 Dec, 1-2 Jan no new arrivals) Last arrival 22.00hrs Last dep noon

A wildlife enthusiast's paradise where facility buildings blend in with the environment. Beecraigs is situated in open countryside in the Bathgate Hills. Small bays with natural shading offer intimate pitches, and there's a restaurant serving lunch and dinner. Toilet block includes en suite facilities. A 6 acre site with 36 touring pitches, 36 hardstandings.

Leisure: **Facilities:** **Services:** **Within 3 miles:** **Notes:** No cars by tents No ball games near caravans, no noise after .22.00hrs. Children's bath. Country park facilities

CRAIGNURE

►►►► 76% Shieling Holidays

PA65 6AY

☎ 01680 812496

e-mail: info@shielingholidays.co.uk

web: www.shielingholidays.co.uk

dir: *From ferry left onto A849 to Iona. 400mtrs left at church, follow site signs towards sea*

* £15-£17 £15-£17 £14.50-£16

Open Apr-Oct Last arrival 22.00hrs Last departure noon

A lovely site on the water's edge with spectacular views, and less than one mile from ferry landing. Hardstandings and service points are provided for motorhomes, and there are astro-turf pitches for tents. The park also offers unique, en suite cottage tents for hire and bunkhouse accommodation for families. A 7 acre site with 90 touring pitches, 30 hardstandings and 15 statics.

Leisure:

Facilities:

Services:

Within 3 miles:

Notes: Bikes. Wi-fi

DULAS

►►►► 84% Tyddyn Isaf Caravan Park

Lligwy Bay LL70 9PQ

☎ 01248 410203 01248 410667

e-mail: mail@tyddynisaf.co.uk

dir: *Take A5025 through Benllech to Moelfre rdbt, left towards Amlwch to Brynrefail village. Turn right opposite craft shop. Site 0.5m down lane on right*

Open Mar-Oct (rs Mar-Jul & Sep-Oct bar & shop opening limited) Last arrival 21.30hrs Last departure 11.00hrs

A beautifully situated, spacious family park on rising ground next to a sandy beach, with views of Lligwy Bay. A private footpath leads to the beach and there is a nature trail around the park. There are good toilet facilities, two family rooms, a well-stocked shop, and café/bar serving meals. 50 seasonal touring pitches. 16 acre site with 30 touring pitches, 50 hardstandings and 56 statics.

Leisure: **Facilities:** **Services:** **Within 3 miles:** **Notes:** Dogs must be kept on leads. No groups, maximum 3 units together. Baby changing unit. Wi-fi

LLANBEDRGOCH

►►► 78% Ty Newydd Leisure Park

LL76 8TZ

☎ 01248 450677 01248 450312

e-mail: mike@tynewydd.com

web: www.tynewydd.com

dir: *A5025 from Brittania Bridge. Through Pentraeth, bear left at layby. Site 0.75m on right*

* £15-£32 £15-£32 £15-£32

Open Mar-Oct (rs Mar-Whit & mid Sep-Oct club wknds only, outdoor pool closed) Last arrival 23.30hrs Last departure 10.00hrs

A low-density park with good facilities, including clean and tidy toilets, a newly refurbished restaurant, good swimming pool facilities, and a well-equipped playground for children. The park is close to Benllech Bay, and is set in four acres of lovely countryside. A 4 acre site with 48 touring pitches, 15 hardstandings and 62 statics.

Leisure:

Facilities:

Services:

Within 3 miles:

Notes: Jacuzzi. Wi-fi

MARIAN-GLAS

▶▶▶▶ 94% Home Farm Caravan Park

LL73 8PH

☎ 01248 410614 01248 410900

e-mail: enq@homefarm-anglesey.co.uk

web: www.homefarm-anglesey.co.uk

dir: *On A5025, 2m N of Benllech. Site 300mtrs beyond church*

Open Apr-Oct Last arrival 21.00hrs Last departure noon

A first class park in an elevated and secluded position sheltered by trees, with good planting and landscaping. The peaceful rural setting affords views of farmland, the sea, and the mountains of Snowdonia. The modern toilet blocks are spotlessly clean and well maintained, and there are excellent play facilities for children both indoors and out. The area is blessed with sandy beaches, and local pubs and shops cater for everyday needs. A 6 acre site with 98 touring pitches, 21 hardstandings and 84 statics.

Leisure: **Facilities:** **Services:** **Within 3 miles:** **Notes:** No roller blades, skateboards or scooters

RHOSNEIGR

▶▶▶ 77% Ty Hen

Station Rd LL64 5QZ

☎ 01407 810331 01407 810331

e-mail: info@tyhen.com

web: www.tyhen.com

dir: *From A55 exit 5 follow signs to Rhosneigr, at clock turn right. Entrance 50mtrs before Rhosneigr railway station*

Open mid Mar-Oct Last arrival 21.00hrs Last departure noon

Attractive seaside position near a large fishing lake and riding stables, in lovely countryside. A smart toilet block offers a welcome amenity at this popular family park, where friendly owners are always on hand. 31 seasonal touring pitches available. A 7.5 acre site with 38 touring pitches, 5 hardstandings and 42 statics.

Leisure:

Facilities:

Services:

Within 3 miles:

Notes: 1 motor vehicle per pitch. Dogs must be kept on leads. Children must be in tents/tourers/statics by 22.00hrs. Fishing, family room, walks. Wi-fi

PORTHCAWL

►►► 69% Brodawel Camping & Caravan Park

Moor Ln, Nottage CF36 3EJ

☎ 01656 783231

dir: *M4 junct 37, A4229 towards Porthcawl. Site on right off A4229*

Open Apr-Sep Last arrival 19.00hrs Last departure 11.00hrs

A family run park catering mainly for families, on the edge of the village of Nottage. It is very convenient for Porthcawl and the Glamorgan Heritage Coast, both a 5-minute drive away. A 4 acre site with 100 touring pitches.

Leisure:
Facilities:
Services:
Within 3 miles:
Notes:

LLANDOVERY

►►►► 89% Erwlon Caravan & Camping Park

Brecon Rd SA20 0RD

☎ 01550 721021 & 720332

e-mail: peter@erwlon.co.uk

dir: *0.5m E of Llandovery on A40*

Open all year Last arrival anytime Last departure noon

Long-established family-run site set beside a brook in the Brecon Beacons foothills. The town of Llandovery and the hills overlooking the Towy Valley are a short walk away. The superb, Scandinavian-style facilities block, with cubicled washrooms and family and disabled rooms, is an impressive feature and ongoing improvements include a campers' kitchen. An 8 acre site with 75 touring pitches, 15 hardstandings.

Leisure:
Facilities:
Services:
Within 3 miles:
Notes: Quiet after 22.30hrs. Fishing, bicycle storage & hire. Wi-fi

NEWCASTLE EMLYN

►►►►► 81% Cenarth Falls Holiday Park

Cenarth SA38 9JS

☎ 01239 710345 01239 710344

e-mail: enquiries@cenarth-holipark.co.uk

dir: *Off A484 on outskirts of Cenarth towards Cardigan*

£15-£26 £15-£26 £15-£26

Open Mar-16 Dec Last arrival 20.00hrs Last departure 11.00hrs

A high quality park with excellent facilities, close to the village of Cenarth where the River Teifi (famous for its salmon and sea trout) cascades through the Cenarth Falls Gorge. A well-landscaped park with an indoor heated swimming pool and fitness suite, and a restaurant and bar. A 2 acre site with 30 touring pitches, 30 hardstandings and 89 statics.

Leisure:

Facilities:

Services:

Within 3 miles:

Notes: No dogs from 15 Jul-2 Sep. Pool table, health & leisure complex

NEWCASTLE EMLYN

►►► 83% Argoed Meadow Caravan and Camping Site

Argoed Farm SA38 9JL

☎ 01239 710690

dir: *From Newcastle Emlyn on A484 towards Cenarth, take B4332. Site 300yds on right*

Open all year Last arrival anytime Last departure noon

Pleasant open meadowland on the banks of the River Teifi, very close to Cenarth Falls gorge. A modern toilet block adds to the general appeal. A 3 acre site with 30 touring pitches, 5 hardstandings.

Facilities:

Services:

Within 3 miles:

Notes: Dogs must be kept on leads, no bikes or skateboards

NEWCASTLE EMLYN

►►► 74% Afon Teifi Caravan & Camping Park

Pentrecagal SA38 9HT

☎ 01559 370532

e-mail: afonteifi@btinternet.com

dir: *Signed off A484, 2m E of Newcastle Emlyn*

Open Apr-Oct Last arrival 23.00hrs

Set on the banks of the River Teifi, a famous salmon and sea trout river, this park is secluded with good views. Family owned and run, and only two miles from the market town of Newcastle Emlyn. A 6 acre site with 110 touring pitches, 22 hardstandings and 10 statics.

Leisure:

Facilities:

Services:

Within 3 miles:

Notes: 15 acres of woodland, fields & walks, ball area

ABERAERON

►►► 80% Aeron Coast Caravan Park

North Rd SA46 0JF

☎ 01545 570349 01545 571289

e-mail: enquiries@aeroncoast.co.uk

web: www.aeroncoast.co.uk

dir: *On A487 (coast road) on N edge of Aberaeron, signed. Filling station at entrance*

£15-£24 £15-£24 £15-£24

Open Mar-Oct Last arrival 23.00hrs Last departure 11.00hrs

A well-managed family holiday park on the edge of the attractive resort of Aberaeron, with direct access to the beach. The spacious pitches are all level. On-site facilities include an extensive outdoor pool complex, a multi-activity outdoor sports area, an indoor child play area, a small lounge bar which serves food, a games room and an entertainment suite. A 22 acre site with 100 touring pitches, 23 hardstandings and 200 statics.

Leisure:

Facilities:

Services:

Within 3 miles:

Notes: Families only. No motorcycles. Indoor leisure rooms, entertainment room

BORTH

69% Brynowen Holiday Park

SY24 5LS

☎ 01970 871366 & 871125

e-mail: brynowen@park-resorts.com

dir: *Signed off B4353, S of Borth*

Open Mar-Oct Last arrival 19.00hrs Last departure 10.00hrs

Enjoying spectacular views across Cardigan Bay and the Cambrian Mountains, a small touring park in a large and well-equipped holiday centre. The well-run park offers a wide range of organised activities and entertainment for all the family from morning until late in the evening. A long sandy beach is a few minutes drive away. A 52 acre site with 13 touring pitches and 480 statics.

Leisure:

Facilities:

Services:

Within 3 miles:

Notes: No cars by caravans or tents. Kids' clubs, mini ten-pin bowling

LLANDDULAS

►►►► 86% Bron-Y-Wendon Caravan Park

Wern Rd LL22 8HG

☎ 01492 512903 01492 512903

e-mail: stay@northwales-holidays.co.uk

dir: *Take A55 W. Turn right at sign for Llanddulas A547 junct 23, then sharp right. 200yds, under A55 bridge. Park on left*

* £19-£22 £19-£22

Open all year Last arrival anytime Last departure 11.00hrs

A good quality site with sea views from every pitch, and excellent purpose-built toilet facilities. Staff are helpful and friendly, and everything from landscaping to maintenance has a stamp of excellence. An ideal seaside base for touring Snowdonia, with lots of activities available nearby. An 8 acre site with 130 touring pitches, 85 hardstandings.

Leisure:

Facilities:

Services:

Within 3 miles:

Notes: Tourist information, heated shower blocks, internet access. Wi-fi

LLANRWST

►►►► 87%
Bron Derw Touring Caravan Park

LL26 0YT

☎ 01492 640494 01492 640494

e-mail: bronderw@aol.com

web: www.bronderw-wales.co.uk

dir: *From A55 take A470 for Betwys-y-Coed & Llanwrwst. In Llanwrst left into Parry Rd signed Llanddoged. Left at T-junct, site signed at 1st farm entrance on right*

* £15-£17 £15-£17

Open Mar-Oct Last arrival 22.00hrs Last departure 11.00hrs

At Bron Derw all pitches are fully serviced, and there is a heated toilet block with immaculate facilities. The utility room, set in a modern conservatory alongside the facility block, houses a washing machine, tumble dryer and sinks for washing up and veg preparation. CCTV cameras cover the whole park. A 2.5 acre site with 20 touring pitches, 20 hardstandings.

Facilities: **Services:** **Within 3 miles:** **Notes:** Children must be supervised. No bikes, scooters, skate boards, dogs must be on short leads

TOWYN (NEAR ABERGELE)

72% Ty Mawr Holiday Park

Towyn Rd LL22 9HG

☎ 01745 832079 01745 827454

e-mail: admin.tymawr@parkresorts.com

dir: *On A548, 0.25m W of Towyn*

Open Etr-Oct (rs Apr (excluding Etr)) Last arrival mdnt Last departure 10.00hrs

A very large coastal holiday park with extensive leisure facilities including sports and recreational amenities, and club and eating outlets. The touring facilities are rather dated but clean. A n18 acre site with 400 touring pitches and 464 statics.

Leisure:

Facilities:

Services:

Within 3 miles:

Notes: Free evening entertainment, kids' club

CORWEN

►► 70% Llawr-Betws Farm Caravan Park

LL21 0HD

☎ 01490 460224 & 460296

dir: *3m W of Corwen off A494 (Bala road)*

Open Mar-Oct Last arrival 23.00hrs Last departure noon

A quiet grassy park with mature trees and gently sloping pitches. The friendly owners keep the facilities in good condition. A 12.5 acre site with 35 touring pitches and 68 statics.

Leisure:

Facilities:

Services:

Within 3 miles:

Notes: Fishing

LLANGOLLEN

►► 76% Ty-Ucha Caravan Park

Maesmawr Rd LL20 7PP

☎ 01978 860677

dir: *1m E of Llangollen. Signed 250yds off A5*

Open Etr-Oct Last arrival 22.00hrs Last departure 13.00hrs

A very spacious site in beautiful surroundings, with a small stream on site, and superb views. Ideal for country and mountain walking, and handily placed near the A5. There is a games room with table tennis. A 4 acre site with 40 touring pitches.

Leisure:

Facilities:

Services:

Within 3 miles:

Notes: No tents

PRESTATYN

77% Presthaven Sands

Gronant LL19 9TT

☎ 01745 856471 01745 886646

dir: *A548 from Prestatyn towards Gronant. Site signed. (NB If using Satnav use LL19 9ST)*

* £11-£72 £11-£72

Open mid Mar-Oct (rs mid Mar-May & Sep-Oct facilities may be reduced) Last arrival 20.00hrs Last departure 10.00hrs

Set beside two miles of superb sandy beaches and dunes, this large holiday centre offers extensive leisure and sports facilities and lively entertainment for all the family. The leisure complex houses clubs, swimming pools, restaurants, shops, launderette and pub, and the touring area is separate from the much larger static section. A 21 acre site with 34 touring pitches and 1052 statics.

Leisure:

Facilities:

Services:

Within 3 miles:

Notes: Dogs must be kept on leads at all times, certain dog breeds banned. Kids' clubs. Wi-fi

ABERSOCH

►►► 78% Deucoch Touring & Camping Park

Sarn Bach LL53 7LD

☎ 01758 713293

e-mail: info@deucoch.com

dir: *From Abersoch take Sarn Bach road, at x-rds turn right, site on right in 800yds*

Open Mar-Oct Last arrival 22.00hrs Last departure 11.00hrs

A sheltered site with sweeping views of Cardigan Bay and the mountains, just a mile from Abersoch and a long sandy beach. The facilities block is well maintained, and this site is of special interest to watersports enthusiasts and those touring the Llyn Peninsula. A 5 acre site with 70 touring pitches, 10 hardstandings.

Leisure:

Facilities:

Services:

Within 3 miles:

Notes: Families only

BARMOUTH

►►►► 90% Trawsdir Touring Caravans & Camping Park

Llanaber LL42 1RR

☎ 01341 280999 Fax 01341 280740

e-mail: enquiries@barmouthholidays.co.uk

web: www.barmouthholidays.co.uk

dir: *3m N of Barmouth on A496, just past Wayside pub on right*

* £15-£30 £15-£30 £10-£25

Open Mar-Jan Last arrival 20.00hrs Last departure noon

A quality park with spectacular views to the sea and hills, and very accessible to motor traffic. Facilities are of a very high standard, and include spacious cubicles with showers and washbasins, individual showers, smart toilets, and under-floor heating. tents and caravans have their own designated areas divided by dry-stone walls, and the site is very convenient for large recreational vehicles. Holiday lodges for hire. A 15 acre site with 70 touring pitches, 70 hardstandings.

Leisure: **Facilities:** **Services:** **Within 3 miles:** **Notes:** Families & couples only. Milk/bread etc available from reception. Wi-fi

BETWS GARMON

►►►► 78% Bryn Gloch

LL54 7YY

☎ 01286 650216

e-mail: eurig@bryngloch.co.uk

web: www.bryngloch.co.uk

dir: *On A4085, 5m SE of Caernarfon*

£15-£30 £15-£30 £15-£30

Open all year Last arrival 23.00hrs Last departure 17.00hrs

An excellent family-run site with immaculate modern facilities, and all level pitches in beautiful surroundings. The park offers the best of two worlds, with a bustling holiday atmosphere and peaceful natural surroundings. The 28 acres of level fields are separated by mature hedges and trees, guaranteeing sufficient space for families wishing to spread out. There are static holiday caravans for hire and plenty of walks in the area. 40 seasonal touring pitches available. A 28 acre site with 160 touring pitches, 60 hardstandings and 17 statics.

Leisure: **Facilities:** **Services:** **Within 3 miles:** **Notes:** Family bathroom, mother & baby room. Wi-fi

CAERNARFON

►►► 77% Cwm Cadnant Valley

Cwm Cadnant Valley, Llanberis Rd LL55 2DF

☎ 01286 673196 01286 675941

e-mail: aa@cwmcadnant.co.uk

web: www.cwmcadnant.co.uk

dir: *On outskirts of Caernarfon on A4086 towards Llanberis, next to fire station*

* £12-£18 £12-£18 £9-£15

Open 14 Mar-3 Nov Last arrival 22.00hrs Last departure 11.00hrs

Set in an attractive wooded valley with a stream is this terraced site with secluded pitches, a good camping area for backpackers and clean, modernised toilet facilities. It is located on the outskirts of Caernarfon, close to the main Caernarfon-Llanberis road and just ten minutes walk from the castle. 5 seasonal touring pitches available. A 4.5 acre site with 60 touring pitches.

Leisure:

Facilities:

Services:

Within 3 miles:

Notes: Family room with baby changing facilities

CRICCIETH

►►►► 81% Eisteddfa

Eisteddfa Lodge, Pentrefelin LL52 0PT

☎ 01766 522696

e-mail: eisteddfa@criccieth.co.uk

dir: *From Porthmadog take A497 towards Criccieth. After approx 3.5m, through Pentrefelin, site signed 1st right after Plas Gwyn Nursing Home*

Open Mar-Oct Last arrival 22.30hrs Last departure 11.00hrs

A quiet, secluded park on elevated ground, sheltered by the Snowdonia Mountains and with lovely views of Cardigan Bay; Criccieth is nearby. The owners are carefully improving the park whilst preserving its unspoilt beauty, and are keen to welcome families, who will appreciate the cubicled facilities. There's a field and play area, woodland walks, a tipi and three static holiday caravans for hire. A 11 acre site with 100 touring pitches, 17 hardstandings.

Leisure:

Facilities:

Services:

Within 3 miles:

Notes: Football pitch, baby bath

DINAS DINLLE

►►►► 84% Dinlle Caravan Park

LL54 5TW

☎ 01286 830324 01286 831526

e-mail: enq@thornleyleisure.co.uk

dir: *S on A499 turn right at sign for Caernarfon Airport. 2m W of Dinas Dinlle coast*

£10-£22 £10-£22 £10-£22

Open Mar-Oct Last arrival 23.00hrs Last departure noon

A very accessible, well-kept grassy site, adjacent to sandy beach, with good views to Snowdonia. The park is situated in acres of flat grassland, with plenty of room for even the largest groups. A lounge bar and family room are comfortable places in which to relax, and children are well provided for with an exciting adventure playground. The beach road gives access to the golf club, a nature reserve, and to Air World at Caernarfon Airport. 50 seasonal touring pitches available. A 20 acre site with 175 touring pitches, 20 hardstandings and 167 statics.

Leisure:
Facilities:
Services:
Within 3 miles:
Notes: Wi-fi

LLANDWROG

►►►► 75% White Tower Caravan Park

LL54 5UH

☎ 01286 830649 & 07802 562785

01286 830649

e-mail: whitetower@supanet.com

web: www.whitetower.supanet.com

dir: *1.5m from village on Tai'r Eglwys road. From Caernarfon take A487 (Porthmadog road). Cross rdbt, 1st right. Site 3m on right*

* £18-£25 £18-£25 £18-£25

Open Mar-10 Jan (rs Mar-mid May & Sep-Oct bar open wknds only) Last arrival 23.00hrs Last departure noon

There are lovely views of Snowdonia from this park located just two miles from the nearest beach at Dinas Dinlle. A well-maintained toilet block has key access, and the hard pitches have water and electricity. Popular amenities include an outdoor heated swimming pool, a lounge bar with family room, and a games and TV room. Seasonal touring pitches available. A 6 acre site with 104 touring pitches, 80 hardstandings and 54 statics.

Leisure: **Facilities:**
Services:
Within 3 miles:

PORTHMADOG

76% Greenacres

Black Rock Sands, Morfa Bychan LL49 9YF

☎ 01766 512781 01766 512781

e-mail: lizzie.sayer@bourne-leisure.co.uk

dir: *From Porthmadog High Street follow Black Rock Sands signs between Factory Shop & Post Office. Park 2m on left at end of Morfa Bychan*

* £14-£92 £14-£92

Open mid Mar-Oct (rs mid Mar-May & Sep-Oct some facilities may be reduced) Last arrival anytime Last departure 10.00hrs

Quality holiday park on level ground close to Black Rock Sands and Snowdonia National Park. Touring pitches are on hardstandings surrounded by grass, and near the entertainment complex. There is a full programme of entertainment, organised clubs, indoor and outdoor sports and leisure, pubs, shows and cabarets. A bowling alley and a large shop/bakery are available. 20 seasonal touring pitches. 121 acre site with 52 touring pitches, 52 hardstandings and 370 statics.

Leisure: **Facilities:** **Services:** **Within 3 miles:** **Notes:** Certain dog breeds banned

PWLLHELI

68% Hafan Y Mor Holiday Park

LL53 6HJ

☎ 0871 231 0887 01766 810379

dir: *From Caernarfon A499 to Pwllheli. A497 to Porthmadog. Park on right, approx 3m from Pwllheli. Or from Telford, A5, A494 to Bala. Right for Porthmadog. Left at rdbt in Porthmadog signed Criccieth & Pwllheli. Park on left 3m from Criccieth*

* £14-£86 £14-£86

Open 20 Mar-2 Nov (rs Mar-May & Sep-Oct reduced facilities) Last arrival 21.00hrs Last departure 10.00hrs

Set between Pwllheli and Criccieth on the Llyn Peninsula, this is an all-action caravan park with direct beach access. Facilities include an indoor splash pool, wave rider, aqua jet racer, and boating lake. The touring area with good portaloos is temporary as there are plans to fully develop a separate touring area. 5 seasonal touring pitches. A 500 acre site with 73 touring pitches and 800 statics.

Leisure: **Facilities:** **Services:** **Within 3 miles:** **Notes:** Fishing. Wi-fi

PWLLHELI

►►► 72% Abererch Sands Holiday Centre

LL53 6PJ

☎ 01758 612327 01758 701556

e-mail: enquiries@abererch-sands.co.uk

dir: *On A497 (Porthmadog to Pwllheli road), 1m from Pwllheli*

£22-£24 £21-£23 £21-£23

Open Mar-Oct Last arrival 21.00hrs Last departure 21.00hrs

Glorious views of Snowdonia and Cardigan Bay can be enjoyed from this very secure, family-run site adjacent to a railway station and a 4-mile stretch of sandy beach. A large heated indoor swimming pool, snooker room, pool room, fitness centre and children's play area make this an ideal holiday venue. An 85 acre site with 70 touring pitches, 70 hardstandings and 90 statics.

Leisure:

Facilities:

Services:

Within 3 miles:

Notes: Wi-fi

FISHGUARD

►►► 84% Fishguard Bay Caravan & Camping Park

Garn Gelli SA65 9ET

☎ 01348 811415 01348 811425

e-mail: enquiries@fishguardbay.com

web: www.fishguardbay.com

dir: *If approaching Fishguard from Cardigan on A487 ignore Satnav to turn right. Turn at sign to campsite. (Single track road with grass in places)*

* £15-£18 £15-£18 £14-£21

Open Mar-9 Jan Last arrival after noon Last departure noon

Set high up on cliffs with outstanding views of Fishguard Bay, and the Pembrokeshire Coastal Path running right through the centre. The park is extremely well kept, with three good toilet blocks, a common room with TV, a lounge/library, decent laundry, and well-stocked shop. A 5 acre site with 50 touring pitches, 4 hardstandings and 50 statics.

Leisure:

Facilities:

Services:

Within 3 miles:

Notes: Wi-fi

HASGUARD CROSS

►►► 81%

Hasguard Cross Caravan Park

SA62 3SL

☎ 01437 781443 01437 781443

e-mail: hasguard@aol.com

dir: *From Haverfordwest take B4327 towards Dale. In 7m right at x-rds. Site 1st right*

Open all year (rs Aug tent field for 28 days) Last arrival 21.00hrs Last departure 10.00hrs

A very clean, efficient and well-run site in Pembrokeshire National Park just 1.5 miles from the sea and beach at Little Haven, and with views of the surrounding hills. The toilet and shower facilities are immaculately clean, and there is a licensed bar (evenings only) serving a good choice of food. A 4.5 acre site with 12 touring pitches and 42 statics.

Facilities:

Services:

Within 3 miles:

Notes: Football field

ST DAVID'S

►► 77%

Tretio Caravan & Camping Park

SA62 6DE

☎ 01437 781600 01437 781594

e-mail: info@tretio.com

dir: *From St David's take A487 towards Fishguard, keep left at Rugby Football Club, straight on 3m. Site signed, turn left to site*

£10-£22 £10-£22 £7-£22

Open Mar-Oct Last arrival 20.00hrs Last departure 10.00hrs

An attractive site in a very rural spot with distant country views, and beautiful local beaches. A mobile shop calls daily at peak periods, and the cathedral city of St David's is only three miles away. A 6.5 acre site with 10 touring pitches and 30 statics.

Leisure:

Facilities:

Services:

Within 3 miles:

Notes: Dogs kept on leads at all times. Pitch & putt, ball games area

TENBY

79% Kiln Park Holiday Centre

Marsh Rd SA70 7RB

☎ 01834 844121 📠 01834 845159

e-mail: sue.james@bourne-leisure.co.uk

dir: *Follow A477/A478 to Tenby for 6m, then follow signs to Penally, site 0.5m on left*

* £11-£92 £11-£92 £11-£66

Open mid Mar-Oct (rs mid Mar-May & Sep-Oct some facilities may be reduced) Last arrival 22.00hrs Last departure 10.00hrs

A large holiday complex complete with leisure and sports facilities, and lots of entertainment for all the family. There are bars and cafés, and plenty of security. This touring, camping and static site is on the outskirts of town, with a short walk through dunes to the sandy beach. The well-equipped toilet block is very clean. Seasonal touring pitches available. A 103 acre site with 193 touring pitches and 703 statics.

Leisure: **Facilities:** **Services:**

Within 3 miles:

Notes: No dogs Jul & Aug, certain dog breeds banned. Entertainment complex, bowling & putting green. Wi-fi

TENBY

►►►► 81% Trefalun Park

Devonshire Dr, St Florence SA70 8RD

☎ 01646 651514 & 0500 655314

📠 01646 651746

e-mail: trefalun@aol.com

dir: *1.5m NW of St Florence & 0.5m N of B4318*

* £13-£22 £13-£22 £11-£19

Open Etr-Oct Last arrival 19.00hrs Last departure noon

Set within 12 acres of sheltered, well-kept grounds, this quiet country park offers well-maintained level grass pitches separated by bushes and trees, with plenty of space to relax in. Children can feed the park's friendly pets. Plenty of activities are available at the nearby Heatherton Country Sports Park, including go-karting, indoor bowls, golf and bumper boating. 35 seasonal touring pitches available. A 12 acre site with 90 touring pitches, 54 hardstandings and 10 statics.

Leisure:

Facilities:

Services:

Within 3 miles:

Notes: No motorised scooters

TENBY

►►►► 78% Well Park Caravan & Camping Site

SA70 8TL

☎ 01834 842179 📠 01834 842179

e-mail: enquiries@wellparkcaravans.co.uk

dir: *Off A478 on right approx 1.5m before Tenby*

* £14-£26 £14-£26 ▲ £12-£18

Open Mar-Oct (rs Mar-mid Jun & mid Sep-Oct bar, launderette, baby room may be closed) Last arrival 22.00hrs Last departure 11.00hrs

An attractive park with good landscaping from trees, ornamental shrubs, and attractive flower borders. The amenities include a launderette and indoor dishwashing, games room with table tennis, and an enclosed play area. A 10 acre site with 100 touring pitches, 14 hardstandings and 42 statics.

Leisure:

Facilities:

Services:

Within 3 miles:

Notes: Family parties only. TV hookups

TENBY

►►► 75% Wood Park Caravans

New Hedges SA70 8TL

☎ 0845 129 8314 & 129 8344 (winter)

e-mail: info@woodpark.co.uk

dir: *At rdbt 2m N of Tenby follow A478 towards Tenby, then take 2nd right & right again*

* £12-£24 £12-£24 ▲ £11-£22

Open Spring BH-Sep (rs mid-end Sep laundrette & games room may not be open) Last arrival 22.00hrs Last departure 10.00hrs

Situated in beautiful countryside between the popular seaside resorts of Tenby and Saundersfoot, and with Waterwynch Bay just a 15-minute walk away, this peaceful site provides a spacious area and relaxing atmosphere for holidays. The slightly sloping touring area is partly divided by shrubs into three paddocks. 12 seasonal touring pitches available. A 10 acre site with 60 touring pitches, 40 hardstandings and 90 statics.

Leisure:

Facilities:

Services:

Within 3 miles:

Notes: Only 1 car per unit, only small dogs accepted, no dogs Jul-Aug & BHs

BRECON

►►►► 77% Bishops Meadow Caravan Park

Bishops Meadow, Hay Rd LD3 9SW

☎ 01874 610000 01874 622090

e-mail: enquiries@bishops-meadow.co.uk

dir: *From A470 (just N of Brecon) take B4602. Site on right*

Open Mar-Oct

A family site with most pitches enjoying spectacular views of the Brecon Beacons. The site has its own outdoor swimming pool, and next door to the park is an all day restaurant with a lounge bar open in the evenings. Facilities include two good quality amenity blocks. The attractions of Brecon are just under two miles from the park. A 3.5 acre site with 82 touring pitches, 24 hardstandings.

Leisure:

Facilities:

Services:

Within 3 miles:

LLANGORS

►►► 72% Lakeside Caravan Park

LD3 7TR

☎ 01874 658226

e-mail: holidays@llangorselake.co.uk

dir: *Exit A40 at Bwlch onto B4560 towards Talgarth. Site signed towards lake in Llangors centre*

* £11.50-£13.50 £11.50-£13.50 £11.50-£13.50

Open Etr or Apr-Oct (rs Mar-May & Oct clubhouse, restaurant, shop limited) Last arrival 21.30hrs Last departure 10.00hrs

Next to Llangors common and lake this attractive park has launching and mooring facilities and is an ideal centre for water sports enthusiasts. Popular with families, and offering a clubhouse/bar, with a well-stocked shop and café/takeaway next door. Boats, bikes and windsurf equipment can be hired on site. A 2 acre site with 40 touring pitches, 8 hardstandings and 72 statics.

Leisure:

Facilities:

Services:

Within 3 miles:

Notes: No pets in hire caravans, no open fires. Windsurfing, fishing from boats

MIDDLETOWN

►►► 77%
Bank Farm Caravan Park

SY21 8EJ

☎ 01938 570526

e-mail: bankfarmcaravans@yahoo.co.uk

dir: *13m W of Shrewsbury, 5m E of Welshpool on A458*

Open Mar-Oct Last arrival 20.00hrs

An attractive park on a small farm, maintained to a high standard. There are two touring areas, one on either side of the A458, and each with its own amenity block, and immediate access to hills, mountains and woodland. A pub serving good food, and a large play area are nearby. A 2 acre site with 40 touring pitches and 33 statics.

Leisure:

Facilities:

Services:

Within 3 miles:

Notes: Coarse fishing pool, jacuzzi, snooker room

SWANSEA

77% Riverside Caravan Park

Ynys Forgan Farm, Morriston SA6 6QL

☎ 01792 775587 01792 795751

e-mail: reception@riversideswansea.com

dir: *Exit M4 junct 45 towards Swansea. Left into private road signed to site*

Open all year (rs Winter months pool & club closed) Last arrival mdnt Last departure noon

A large and busy park close to the M4 but in a quiet location beside the River Taw. This friendly family orientated park has a licensed club and bar with a full high-season entertainment programme. There is a choice of eating outlets with the clubhouse restaurant, takeaway or chip shop. The park has a good indoor pool. A 5 acre site with 90 touring pitches and 256 statics.

Leisure:

Facilities:

Services:

Within 3 miles:

Notes: Dogs by prior arrangement only (no aggressive dog breeds permitted). Fishing on site by arrangement. Wi-fi

LLANTWIT MAJOR

►►► 82% Acorn Camping & Caravan Site

Ham Lane South CF61 1RP

☎ 01446 794024

e-mail: info@acorncamping.co.uk

dir: *B4265 to Llantwit Major, follow camping signs. Approach site through Ham Manor residential park*

Open Feb-8 Dec Last arrival 21.00hrs Last departure 11.00hrs

A peaceful country site in level meadowland, with some individual pitches divided by hedges and shrubs. About one mile from the beach, which can be approached by a clifftop walk, and the same distance from the historic town of Llantwit Major. An internet station and a full size snooker table are useful amenities. A 5.5 acre site with 90 touring pitches, 10 hardstandings and 15 statics.

Leisure:
Facilities:
Services:
Within 3 miles:
Notes: No noise 23.00hrs-07.00hrs. Wi-fi

EYTON

►►►►► 90% The Plassey Leisure Park

The Plassey LL13 0SP

☎ 01978 780277 01978 780019

e-mail: enquiries@plassey.com

web: www.plassey.com

dir: *From A483 at Bangor-on-Dee exit onto B5426 for 2.5m. Site entrance signed on left*

£14-£23.50 £14-£23.50 £14-£23.50

Open Feb-Nov Last arrival 20.30hrs Last departure 18.00hrs

Large park set in in the Dee Valley. Toilet facilities include individual cubicles, while the farm buildings have been converted into a restaurant, coffee shop, and beauty studio. Facilities include scenic walks, free fishing, and use of a golf course. 60 seasonal touring pitches. 10 acre site with 90 touring pitches, 45 hardstandings and 15 statics.

Leisure: **Facilities:** **Services:** **Within 3 miles:**
Notes: No footballs, bikes or skateboards, dogs must be kept on leads. Sauna, badminton & table tennis. Wi-fi

ANTRIM

►►► 78% Six Mile Water Caravan Park

Lough Rd BT41 4DG

☎ 028 9446 4963

e-mail: sixmilewater@antrim.gov.uk

web: www.antrim.gov.uk/caravanpark

dir: *1m from town centre, follow Antrim Forum/Loughshore Park signs. On Dublin road take Lough road (pass Antrim Forum on right). Site at end of road on right*

* £17 £17 £11-£17

Open Mar-Oct Last arrival 21.45hrs Last departure noon

A pretty tree-lined site in a large municipal park, within walking distance of Antrim and the Antrim Forum leisure complex yet very much in the countryside. The modern toilet block is well equipped, and other facilities include a laundry and electric hook-ups. A 9.6 acre site with 44 touring pitches, 20 hardstandings.

Leisure: **Facilities:** **Services:** **Within 3 miles:** **Notes:** Max stay 7 nights. No noise between 22.00hrs-08.00hrs. Dogs must be under control & on leads. Watersports, angling stands & launching facilities

BALLYCASTLE

►►► 71% Watertop Farm

188 Cushendall Rd BT54 6RN

☎ 028 2076 2576

e-mail: watertopfarm@aol.com

dir: *Off A2 from Ballycastle towards Cushendall. Opposite Ballypatrick forest*

£16 £16 £8

Open Etr-Oct (rs Etr-Jun & Sep-Oct farm activities not available)

Located on a family hill sheep farm set in the glens of Antrim. The farm offers a range of activities and attractions including pony trekking, boating, pedal go karts, farm tours, tea room and lots more. The touring facilities consist of three individual sections, two reserved for caravans and the other for tents. The toilets are housed in a converted traditional Irish cottage, and the attached small rural museum serves as a night time social area. A 0.5 acre site with 14 touring pitches, 9 hardstandings.

Leisure:

Facilities:

Services:

Within 3 miles:

Notes: No camp fires, no BBQ trays on grass

BUSHMILLS

►►►►► 87%

Ballyness Caravan Park

40 Castlecatt Rd BT57 8TN

☎ 028 2073 2393 028 2073 2713

e-mail: info@ballynesscaravanpark.com

web: www.ballynesscaravanpark.com

dir: *0.5m S of Bushmills on B66, follow signs*

* £20 £20

Open 17 Mar-Oct Last arrival 21.00hrs Last departure noon

A quality park with superb toilet and other facilities, on farmland beside St Columb's Rill, the stream that supplies the famous nearby Bushmills distillery. The friendly owners built this park with the discerning camper in mind, and they continue to improve it to ever higher standards. There is a pleasant walk around several ponds, and the park is peacefully located close to the beautiful north Antrim coast. A 16 acre site with 48 touring pitches, 48 hardstandings and 50 statics.

Leisure: **Facilities:** **Services:** **Within 3 miles:** **Notes:** No skateboards or roller blades. Family room with bath, library, internet access. Wi-fi

CUSHENDUN

►►► 77%

Cushendun Caravan Park

14 Glendun Rd BT44 0PX

☎ 028 2176 1254 028 2076 2515

e-mail: cushenduncp@moyle-council.org

dir: *From A2 take B92 for 1m towards Glenarm, clearly signed*

Open Apr-Sep Last arrival 22.00hrs Last departure 12.30hrs

A pretty little grassy park surrounded by trees, with separate secluded areas offering some privacy, and static vans discreetly interspersed with tourers. The beautiful north Antrim coast is short drive away through scenic country. A 3 acre site with 12 touring pitches and 64 statics.

Leisure:

Facilities:

Services:

Within 3 miles:

Notes: Dogs must be kept on leads at all times

IRVINESTOWN

►►►► 84% Castle Archdale Caravan Park & Camping Site

Lisnarick BT94 1PP

☎ 028 6862 1333 028 6862 1176

e-mail: info@castlearchdale.com

dir: *Site off B82 (Enniskillen to Kesh road). 10m from Enniskillen*

£20-£25 £20-£25 £15-£20

Open Apr-Oct (rs Apr-Jun & Sep-Oct shop, restaurant & bar open wknds only) Last departure 14.00hrs

On the shores of Lower Loch Erne amidst very scenic countryside, this site is ideal for watersports enthusiasts with its marina and launching facilities. Other amenities available on the site include pony trekking, pedal go-karting, cycle hire and coarse fishing. The toilet facilities are very good. An 11 acre site with 158 touring pitches, 110 hardstandings and 139 statics.

Leisure:

Facilities:

Services:

Within 3 miles:

Notes: No open fires, dogs must be kept on leads. Wi-fi

BALLINSPITTLE

►►►► 74% Garrettstown House Holiday Park

☎ 021 4778156 & 4775286

021 4778156

e-mail: reception@garrettstownhouse.com

dir: *6m from Kinsale, through Ballinspittle, past school & football pitch on main road to beach. Beside stone estate entrance*

Open 4 May-9 Sep (rs Early season-1 Jun shop closed) Last arrival 22.00hrs Last departure noon

Elevated holiday park with tiered camping areas and superb panoramic views. Plenty of on-site amenities, and close to beach and forest park. A 7 acre site with 60 touring pitches, 20 hardstandings and 80 statics.

Leisure:

Facilities:

Services:

Within 3 miles:

Notes: Children's club, crazy golf, video shows, snooker

BALLYLICKEY

►►►► 77% Eagle Point Caravan and Camping Park *(V995535)*

☎ 027 50630

e-mail: eaglepointcamping@eircom.net

dir: *N71 to Bandon, then R586 to Bantry, then N71. 4m to Glengarriff, opposite petrol station*

€26-€28 €26-€28 €26-€28

Open 23 Apr-27 Sep Last arrival 22.00hrs Last departure noon

An immaculate park set in an idyllic position in an outstandingly beautiful area overlooking the rugged bays and mountains of West Cork. Boat launching facilities and small pebble beaches. A 20 acre site with 125 touring pitches.

Leisure:

Facilities:

Services:

Within 3 miles:

Notes: No commercial vehicles, bikes, skates, scooters or jet skis

CLONDALKIN

►►►► 73% Camac Valley Tourist Caravan & Camping Park

Green Isle Rd

☎ 01 4640644 01 4640643

e-mail: info@camacvalley.com

dir: *M50 junct 9, W on N7, site on right of dual carriageway after 2km. Site signed from N7*

Open all year Last arrival anytime Last departure noon

A pleasant lightly wooded park with good layout, facilities and security, within an hour's drive or bus ride of city centre. A 15 acre site with 163 touring pitches, 113 hardstandings.

Leisure:

Facilities:

Services:

Within 3 miles: